Kama Sutra & Tantric Sex

A 2-in-1 Guide to Better Sex

By: More Sex More Fun Book Club

Table of Contents

Kama Sutra

The History About Kama Sutra And Ancient Love Making Techniques

Introduction

For many people when they hear the term Kama Sutra, they immediately think of a borderline pornographic book full of illicit sex positions that only people who are incredibly flexible would ever try. However, this is not all that the Kama Sutra is. In reality, the Kama Sutra presents itself as a guide on how to live a virtuous and gracious life with emphasis on the nature of love, family life and other aspects of the pleasure oriented aspects of the human life. Ultimately, only twenty percent of the Kama Sutra is about sexual positions.

The Kama Sutra is one of three ancient texts that were written in the Sanskrt language to describe the goals of life. Written by a north Indian scholar by the name of Vatsyayna Mallanaga, the Kama Sutra was written in the second century CE and literally means the Treatise on Pleasure. The majority of the book is about philosophy and the theory of love. It covers what triggers love, what sustains love and when it is good or bad.

This book is aimed to guide you through the ancient text of the Kama Sutra and show you how you can use its teachings to bring passion and happiness into your relationships. We are also going to cover briefly on some of the sex positions of the kama sutra, and how they can bring more intimacy into your relationships.

Chapter 1: Kama Sutra – A Brief Look At What It Is And Where It Came From

The Kama Sutra documents the sociology of sex as it was in India many centuries ago. It is a famous book that has been translated many times over. Many people consider the Kama Sutra to be unoriginal and believe that the author, Vatsyana Mallanaga most likely was a reworking of the manuals that already existed in order to write his work. Even so, the Kama Sutra is brings attention to what sexual relationships mean between two people, while still recognizing that that some things are forbidden.

The Kama Sutra encompassed there are sixty-four arts and they were meant to be used by the upper society The text provides detailed descriptions of the rules that both men and women were expected to follow. The rules governed sensuous physical relationships as well as the love and marriage of the couple according to the Hindu law.

While the overall essence of the text relates to being sensuous, the Kama Sutra also ascribes to the traditions and religion of the Hindu society. The primary teaching of the Kama Sutra was that marriages are meant to be happy. Both men and women were to be well versed in the arts of both physical and mental pleasure. The philosophy of the Kama Sutra follows achievements in Dharma, which is religion; Art, which is wealth; Kama, which is pleasures;

and Moksha which is salvation. These are the basic goals that govern life.

The Kama Sutra teaches that all aspects of life are of equal importance and that no aspect should take priority over any other. In order to attain a meaningful life, it is imperative that balance is achieved. If you are able to achieve this balance, you are considered to be living the good life. The Kama Sutra explains that sexuality and erotica are important to human existence and are considered the same as eating. While eating keeps the body alive, sexuality help mankind to propagate.

There are many different stories in ancient Indian scripture that tell about how the Kama Sutra was originated. Below are a couple of examples.

One of the stories that can be found tells that the diety Prjapati, who was the God of Creation, initially declared the ten thousand chapters of the Kama Sutra. The chapters were then assembled by Lord Shiva. Following this, they were further condensed into a great number of chapters. named Shvetaketu. In this story, the role of Vatsyayana was to transcribe the Kama Sutra in Sanskrit.

Another story tells that the Kama Sutra was bestowed on the world by the Indian God Shiva's doorkeeper, Nandi. Nandi, who was a sacred bull, overheard Nandi and his wife, Parvati, while they were making love. Nandi was so inspired that he made an utterance, which was later passed down to humans.

Regardless of where it originated, the Kama Sutra is a book about finding the right partner, maintaining power in a marriage and the art of living. What is unique about the Kama Sutra is that, contrary to popular belief, it does not see women as being erotic subjects, and instead sees them as sexual beings who possess emotions and feelings, which a man should understand in order to achieve the full enjoyment of erotic pleasure.

The Kama Sutra is considered to be the original study of sexuality and quickly became the main resource of subsequent compilations, including the Ananga-Ranga, which is a fifteenth century revised version of the Kama Sutra. However, since it was written in a complex style of Sanskrit it failed to reach readers and fell into obscurity until the late nineteenth century.

One interesting fact about the Kama Sutra is that is actually teaches that the man in a relationship should not sexually approach a woman for the first three nights of the marriage. Instead, he should use this time to understand her feelings, earn her trust and arouse her love. Vatsyayana took a huge leap in the history of Indian sexuality by introducing the idea of love in sex.

In the late nineteenth century, the Kama Sutra began to again gain prominence in India. This occured after a noted linguist and Arabic translator, Sir Richard Burten began working with both Indian and British collaborators to produce an English translation of the Anaga-Ranga. In the translation, Burton made many references to Vatsyayana which led back to the Kama Sutra, and eventually an

English translation of the Kama Sutra was produced as well.

Due to the nature of the content, the Kama Sutra was not legally published in England or the United States until 1962. From the time it was first published in 1883, until it was legally published in 1962, the Kama Sutra gained status as one of the most pirated books in the English language.

Sir Richard Burton's version of the Kama Sutra is the is one of the most well known versions. Not just in the United States but also in India and Europe. Many Hindi and other Indian translations come from Burton's English translation instead of the original Sanskrit source. However, because of this, the true essence of the Kama Sutra has been lost. Where the original Kama Sutra emphasized the importance of the female and her role in the act of lovemaking, Burton's version silences the woman.

The Kama Sutra contains sixty-four arts of love which are made up of acts of love and sexual congress divided into eight methods. The Kama Sutra also explores the pleasures of the woman, as well as heterosexuality, and homosexuality. A few of the other topics the book covers include how to attract a spouse, how to be a good wife and how to strengthen the bonds between people to avoid the need to seek out a different domestic situation.

One of the most basic tenents for Kama Sutra is so there is marriage in relationships so both parties are happy both physically and cerebrally. Some of the topics that Kama Sutra explores are the social concepts for sexual union, getting a wife and about wives and other men. You will also learn about how to attract others to you. In the end, you will learn how to win over someone of the opposite sex. If someone has rejected you, you will learn about that as well.

There are some who believe that you can use the Kama Sutra as a manual for your marriage. While this would be awesome, the Kama Sutra is nowhere near good advice for a monogamous relationship. As you go about reading the Kama Sutra, you are going to realize that the main figure is the courtesan who is the master of various ways in how a woman can please her man.

Something unique about the Kama Sutra is that it pays special attention to the creation of pleasure on the woman. Any man who cannot bring about these pleasures is going to be liable to meet recourse from a woman as they go seek pleasure somewhere else.

The Karma Sutra was one of the original studies for sexuality and therefore became the beginning for any other compilations that came after it. One of those compilations was the Ananga Ranga which built upon the basic tenets for what Vatsyayana believed in. Still, the Kama Sutra is one of the most sought after books even thought it is written in Sanskrit.

It was not until the nineteenth century that the Kama Sutra was picked back up and continued from the traditions that were found in India. Around 1870, Sir Richard Burton worked on translating the Ananga Ranga in which they found many references to Vatsyayana. Due to this, he produced an English version of the Kama Sutra and found that it held a lot of proliferations to the translastions and many versions that can be found based on the original text.

Ananga Ranga

This version is from the fifteenth century and is just an updated version of the Kama Sutra. But, it is more easily accessed than the original version of the Kama Sutra. Because of this, it actually bypassed the Kama Sutra for a long time. The Ananga Ranga was commissioned by a nobleman. Surprisingly, the Ananga Ranga was written by a Hindu poet that used the Kama Sutra as inspiration. You can find the Ananga Ranga in Urdu, Arabic, and even Persian.

When you look at the dedication to the Ananga Ranga you will realize that it has a bit of advice for married couples and how they are supposed to work together in social and sexual settings. In this description, it goes on to describe a female body and talks about the different places on a woman's body and how they are supposed to be pleased. Not only that, but you will find how a male and female are supposed to work together in order to increase their pleasure.

Chapter 2: The Sixty-Four Arts Of The Kama Sutra

Now that we have a general idea of where the Kama Sutra came from as well as what the Kama Sutra truly is, we are going to look a little deeper into the writing to learn what the Kama Sutra teaches. We are going to start with the sixty-four arts of the Kama Sutra.

Vatsyayana listed out sixty-four arts that were make it to where a person appeared more attractive.. These suggestions do not apply to just one gender, which is interesting since many ancient texts tell about the woman making herself attractive for a man, leaving the impression that a man didn't need to do anything to become more attractive for a female.

In the Kama Sutra, Vatsyayana states:

"A public woman, endowed with a good disposition, beauty and other winning qualities, and also versed in the above arts, obtains the name of a Ganika, or public woman of high quality, and receives a seat of honour in an assemblage of men.She is, moreover, always respected by the king, and praised by learned men, and her favour being sought for by all, she becomes an object of universal regard. The daughter of a king too as well as the daughter of a minister, being learned in the above arts, can make their husbands favorable to them, even though these may have thousands of other wives besides themselves.If a wife becomes separated from her husband, and falls into

distress, she can support herself easily, even in a foreign country, by means of her knowledge of these arts. Even the bare knowledge of them gives attractiveness to a woman, though the practice of them may be only possible or otherwise according to the circumstances of each case. A man who is versed in these arts, who is loquacious and acquainted with the arts of gallantry, gains very soon the hearts of women, even though he is only acquainted with them for a short time."

Here is a list of the 64 arts; they are going to be listed in Sanskrit as well as English.

1. Geet Vidya – Art of singing

2. Vadya vidya – Art of playing on musical instruments

3. Nritya vidya – Art of dancing

4. Natya vidya – Art of theatricals

5. Alekhya vidya – Art of painting

6. Viseshakacchedya vidya- Art of paining the face and body with color

7. Tandula-kusuma-bali-vikara – Art of preparing offerings from rice and flowers

8. Pushpastarana – Art of making a covering of flowers for a bed

9. Dasana-vasananga-raga – Art of applying preparations for cleansing teeth cloths and painting the body

10. Mani-bhumika-karma – Art of making the groundwork of jewels

11. Aayya-racana- Art of covering the bed

12. Udaka-vadya – Art of playing music on water

13. Udaka-ghata – Art of splashing with water

14. Citra-yoga – Are of practically applying an admixture of colors

15. Malya-grathana-vikalpa – Art of designing a preparation of wreaths

16. Sekharapida-yojana – Art of practically setting the coronet on the head

17. Nepathya-yoga – Art of practically dressing in the tiring room

18. Karnapatra-bhanga – Art of decorating the tragus of the ear

19. Sugandha-yukti – Art of practical application of aromatics

20. Bhushana-yojana – Art of applying or setting ornaments

21. Aindra-jala – Art of juggling

21. Kaucumara – A kind of art

23. Hasta-laghava – Art of sleight of hand

24. Citra-sakapupa-bhakshya-vikara-kriya – Art of preparing varieties of delicious food

25. Panaka-rasa-ragasava-yojana – Art of practically preparing palatable drinks and tinging draughts with red color.

26. Suci-vaya-karma – Art of needlework and weaving

27. Sutra-krida – Art of playing with thread

28. Vina-damuraka-vadya – Art of playing on the lute and small drum

29. Prahelika – Art of making and solving riddles

30. Durvacaka-yoga – Art of practicing language difficult to be answered by others

31. Pustaka-vacana – Art of reciting books

32. Natikakhyayika-darsana – Art of enacting short plays and anecdotes

33. Kavya-samasya-purana – Art of solving enigmatic verses

34. Pattika-vetra-bana-vikalpa – Art of design and preparation of shield, cane and arrows

35. Tarku-karma – Art of spinning by spindle

36. Takshana – Art of carpentry

37. Vastu-vidya – Art of engineering

38. Raupya-ratna-pariksha – Art of testing silver and jewels

39. Dhatu-vada – Art of metallurgy

40. Mani-raga jnana – Art of tinging jewels

41. Akara jnana – Art of mineralogy

42. Vrikshayur-veda-yoga – Art of practicing medicine or medical treatment by herbs

43. Mesha-kukkuta-lavaka-yuddha-vidhi – Art of knowing the mode of fighting lambs, cocks and birds

44. Suka-sarika-pralapana – Art of maintaining or knowing conversation between male and female cockatoos

45. Utsadana – Art of healing or cleaning a person with perfumes

46. Kesa-marjana-kausala – Art of combing hair

47. Akshara-mushtika-kathana – Art of talking with fingers

48. Dharana-matrika – Art of the use of amulets

49. Desa-bhasha-jnana – Art of knowing provincial dialects

50. Nirmiti-jnana – Art of knowing prediction by heavenly voice

51. Yantra-martika – Art of mechanics

52. Mlecchita-kutarka-vikalpa – Art of fabricating barbarous or foreign sophistry

53. Samvacya – Art of conversation

54. Manasi kavya-kriya – Art of composing verse

55. Kriya-vikalpa – Art of designing a literary work or a medical remedy

56. Chalitka-yoga – Art of practicing as a builder of shrines
57. Abhidhana-kosha-cchando-jnana – Art of the use of lexicography and meters

58. Vastra-gopana – Art of concealment of cloths

59. Dyuta-visesha – Art of knowing specific gambling

60. Akarsha-krida – Art of playing with dice or magnet

61. Balaka-kridanaka – Art of using children's toys

62. Vainayiki vidya – Art of enforcing discipline

63. Vaijayiki vidya – Art of gaining victory

64. Vaitaliki vidya – Art of awakening master with music at dawn

You can see that a lot of these arts would have no place in making you more attractive in today's society, however there are some that are still applicable today.

The purpose behind these arts is not to make a good spouse, instead it is to try and make a person who is going to possess the qualities that some wants in a spouse along with making that person feel good about themselves. Indians in the ancient world paid special attention to the details before they could enjoy intercourse Knowledge of the sixty-four arts was important to ensure that the act of foreplay was carried out correctly. We are going to cover foreplay later on in this book, first we are going to cover how the Kama Sutra can bring happiness and health to your body and your mind.

Chapter 3: Kama Sutra – Bringing Happiness And Health To Your Body And Mind

When it is well practiced, the Kama Sutra is able to bring many health benefits to our physical, physiological and mental well being. There are different reasons behind this, some of which include the yoga basis to the sexual positions, tantric massage, as well as encouraging closer relationships between couples.

There are many benefits to the yoga positioning in the lovemaking aspect to the Kama Sutra. Yoga is well known to provide many benefits from flexibility and relaxation to increased blood flow and mental clarity.

Tantric massage is an erotic massage that encourages partners to really get to know one anothers bodies. By becoming familiar with each other's bodies, partners are able to learn what their partner finds arousing outside of the typical arousal spots.

The encouragement of healthy relationships between partners occurs both in and out of the bedroom. The Kama Sutra recognizes that there is a connection between the intimate parts of a relationship as well as the everyday motions a couple goes through. Being able to connect in and outside of the bedroom helps a couple to establish a nurturing bond that cannot be broken.

There are many other ways that a healthy sex life, as laid out in the Kama Sutra, can contribute to your health and happiness.

When they are done correctly, the Kama Sutra positions are designed to encourage bonding and curiousity between partners. Some of the more advanced positions also foster trust in one another in order to balance and not be hurt. Learning how to pleasure one another is a journey that is exciting and invigorating and allows for new feelings to emerge in the relationship.

Sex also aids in the production of hormones such as oxytocin, which keeps you healthy and glowing. Engaging in one hour of sexual activity is equivalent to fifteen minutes of jogging, and can burn up to two hundred calories per session. Sex is thought to fight stress, increase heart health and those who engage in regular sex are said to be less impacted by arthritis, depression, anxiety, and stress.

This isn't to say that you can go and have sex with anyone in order to reap the benefits of having sex. The Kama Sutra promoted having intimate sex with one partner. In order to have intimate sex, there needs to be a connection on a level deeper than simply physical. There needs to be a mental, emotional and spiritual connection between two partners in order to really get any of the benefits of having sex in the way the Kama Sutra lays out.

Today there are many people who feel as though their sex life has fallen into a rut. The act of making love becomes boring and tedious and couples tend to get lost in the day to day routine of their lives. This was true back in the ancient Indian times as well as today. This was why the Kama Sutra spent a lot of time discussing foreplay.

When a relationship fails to have a healthy sex life, the couple often finds that they will eventually have problems in other aspects of their relationship. The act of making love creates a closeness between a man and woman, and this is what the Kama Sutra was created to cultivate.

The Kama Sutra puts a lot of emphasis on foreplay over the actual act of intercourse. In the Kama Sutra's teachings it is emphasized that foreplay should be taken slowly for many reasons. Some of these reasons include:

- Foreplay makes things hotter in the bedroom and builds the anticipation;

- Foreplay allows the man and woman to get to know one another's bodies;

- Foreplay ensures that both partners are peaking with excitement; and

- Foreplay creates a connection between the two partners.

Many people don't truly understand what foreplay is. In today's society we think that foreplay is simply what we do in the moments leading up to sex, and in many cases people feel as though this is unnecessary. The Kama Sutra, however, recognized that intercourse without foreplay can actually be detrimental to the intimacy that two lovers should feel. The Kama Sutra teaches that great love making begins in the mind and preparing for making love is the most important part of the equation.

In the next couple chapters of this book we are going to analyze what foreplay was intended to be, according to the Kama Sutra, and how you can use that information in your personal life.

Chapter 4: Getting Started With Foreplay And The Kama Sutra

When foreplay was written out in the Kama Sutra, there was reference to the servants and other people who would be in the room to help the man set up the room as well as being the woman to him. In today's society, many of us don't have servants that we can rely on to do these things for us. For that reason, the steps to foreplay have been modified from the way it was written to apply to the Indian culture and times it was written for. Instead they have been written as they would be to apply to the lives of the people who are reading this book to learn how to bring more happiness into their lives and relationships. The steps below may seem like a lot of work to get everything ready, but the preparations are sure to increase the excitement and pleasure you and your partner feel making it worth the effort.

1. The first, and most important thing, that needs to be done before you are intimate with your partner is to take the time to relax. After a long, exhausting day at work, you need to take the time to relax both your body and your mind. This relaxation can be achieved in whatever way you find to be the most effective. This can be a hot shower, a nap, or a run. By taking the time to relax before becoming intimate with your partner you are ensuring that you aren't going to be distracted thinking about your day while you are with your partner.

2. The Kama Sutra refers to the room that you and your partner are going to be intimate in as the pleasure room. The decoration of the pleasure room is an important aspect to ensure that both partners are able to be adequately aroused. While we aren't likely to place garlands and bunches of flowers around the room, you can burn some aromatic candles or incense. Some of the scents you could choose to burn include jasmine, cinnamon, or ylang-ylang. Another way to set the mood in the room is to have tantric music playing in the background. The temperature of the room is very important. You want the temperature to be warm, but not too warm. While you want the room to be comfortable, you don't want it to be so comfortable that you are going to curl up and fall asleep. Keep in mind that you are going to want to eliminate all distractions, including TV's, phones, laptops, beepers, and the doorbell.

3. In the Kama Sutra it is stated that upon entering the pleasure room both partners should be freshly cleansed. The purpose of ensure that you are clean is to make sure that your body is appealing to your partner. This is something that hasn't changed with time. This is also a great opportunity to cleanse your day away and start fresh with your partner.

Wear a perfume that is going to arouse your partners senses. It is important to choose a scent that your partner likes over one that you like. If you are unsure what scents your partner likes, it is advised that you use a neutral scent, or no scent at all. Another suggestion is to wear something that is going to be visually appealing to your partner. This doesn't mean that you need to wear something that is revealing, or even buy something new to wear. You can wear a color that your partner likes, or even an outfit that your partner often compliments.

4. The Kama Sutra strongly encourages that you embrace your partner before making love, however it isn't referring to your everyday hug. When you are embracing according to the Kama Sutra instructions, you are using much more than your arms. You will be touching, rubbing, and pressing with the front part of your body. The Kama Sutra says that you should avoid using your hands to caress, and instead enjoy the touching sensation from one another's bodies. This can be done before you enter your pleasure room, as well as when you are deep into the act of foreplay.

5. Make the bed with clean sheets and pillow cases. Place one pillow on each end of the bed. Next to the bed you should have a couch and a low table or stool that you can place your massage oils as well as any other items you may choose to use.

6. The Kama Sutra encourages you to share a light meal together, Avoid heavy foods, as these are more likely to make you feel uncomfortable and sleepy after you are done eating. Instead you can feed one another small bites of fruits and other aphrodisiac foods. In the original script of the Kama Sutra, Vatsyayana stated that the man would play with the ties that was holding the womans clothing on. This can be easily modified for modern times, with the man running his fingertips along the back of the neckline of the woman's shirt, or if she is

wearing a skirt along the hem of the skirt where her leg begins to show.

7. While you are eating, have a romantic conversations. At this time you should be focused on showing your partner how much you love, trust and care about them. Bring up any past romantic getaways and erotic imagery. Use your words to get their imaginations wild with anticipation. Vatsyayana said that at this time the man would take the woman out onto the balcony and show her the moon and the stars. He would point out the constellations and the conversation would slowly shift from neutral topics with a vague sexual subtext, to more obvious erotic imagery.

Now that you have an idea on how foreplay begins, we are going to take a look at what aphrodisiac foods are and then explore the embraces and kisses that the Kama Sutra outlines as being appropriate for foreplay.

Chapter 5: Aphrodisiac Foods

An aphrodisiac is something that stimulates sexual desire. There are some foods that are believe to stimulate pleasure centers and increase the sex drive and desire of the people eating them. There are different aphrodisiacs in every culture. In the in Kama Sutra, the aphrodisiac foods that were recommended included rice mixed with wild honey as well as a mix of ground up pumpkin seeds, almonds, sugar cane the root of the bamboo that were mixed into milk and honey.

The combinations above may seem a little weird to people today. Below you will find a list of some of the foods that are the typical aphrodisiacs that are used today.

- Avocado: This fruit has been considered an aphrodisiac for a long time. The fruits high levels of vitamin E could be responsible for keeping the spark alive in the bedroom because it was meant to help maintain youth and energy.

- Bananas: Bromelain is an enzyme that is found in bananas and is known to trigger testosterone production. The spike in testosterone helps raise arousal in men.

- Chili Peppers: This bright red spice stimulates endorphins which can give you the same symptoms that you will feel when you are aroused.

- Chocolate: Dark chocolate can give you a chemical spike to make you feel pleasure, this is why chocolate covered fruit is a common choice of dessert foods for couples.

- Coffee: Caffeine is a stimulant that causes more blood to flow through the body. It is also highly thought of to put women into an aroused mood.

- Honey: Honey helps to maintain hormone levels while increasing energy.

- Olive Oil: The Greeks believed that olive oil made men more virile. It is also a great source of monosaturated and polyunsaturated fats which are needed to ensure that you are healthy.

- Oysters: This is probably the first thing people think of when they think of aphrodisiac foods. Oysters contain amino acids that aid in producing the hormones that are needed for sex.

- Pine Nuts: Zinc has been proven to be linked to having a healthy sex drive. Pine nuts are high in zinc, which is why they are considered an aphrodisiac.

- Pumpkin Seeds: These little seeds are incredibly high in magnesium. Magnesium helps to raise the levels of testosterone by ensuring more enters the blood stream.

- Strawberries: This fruit is great to feed to one another as a dessert that will keep the blood flowing to all regions of the body.

- Watermelon: This fruit is thought to have a Viagra like effect on the body because it relaxes blood vessels and as a result improves blood flow.

- Whipped Cream: While there is no scientific reason that whipped cream will boost libido, it can be incredibly erotic to eat with a partner and is sure to put it you in the mood.

There are many other foods that are considered aphrodisiacs, such as figs, cherries, pomegranates, artichokes, arugula and chai tea. With there being so many options you are sure to be able to put together a light meal or snack for you and your partner to enjoy together.

While it is believed that aphrodisiacs are going to actually increase sexual desire, they have been shared across all races and cultures. In essence, an aphrodisiac is the human's way of wanting to find a way for better sex.

Sadly, the FDA has found that there is actually no approach that is no medical that is going to work in increasing someone's sexual desire. But, that does not stop people from believing that an aphrodisiac will work.

Foods are one of the most commonly found aphrodisiacs in the world because they so closely resemble a person's genitalia. As mentioned above, there are a lot of different foods that are considered to be aphrodisiacs. Clams and oysters are most commonly associated with aphrodisiacs because of the way that they are shaped and the texture that the present when they are eaten. But, the truth is that they are going to be high in zinc which is something that many people lack in their diet and eating them causes a person to be more healthy therefore increasing their sex drive.

Spicy foods have given some scientific truth to the fact that food can increase one's sex drive. However, this is because of a spice that is found in cayenne pepper known as capsaicin that causes an increase in heart rate as well as metabolism. There may even be some sweating all of which are going to be similar to symptoms one might experience while they are having sex.

As strange as it sounds, okra is a vegetable that is rich in magnesium but is also a natural relaxant. All of the vitamins that are found in okra are good for your sex organs which can assist in increasing your sex drive. However, eating okra is not going to increase your sex drive just because you have ingested it.

Herbs are not often thought of as food, but they are used to spice food so they are still going into your body. One of the herbs that is most commonly associated with love is ginseng and that is because it resembles a human body. Plus, if you look at the translation of the name, it actually means man root. When ginseng was given to animals, there was an increase in sexual response, but sadly not in humans.

One herb that can be found in India as well as Africa is the Yohimbe which is thought to have the qualities of an aphrodisiac. It is thought that the Yohimbe wll stimulate the nerves that are located in the spine which can cause an erection without the need to increase sexual excitement. This herb is now known as the herbal form of Viagra.

However, if you are going to use this herb, you need to know that there are side effects that can be pretty severe. These side effects are overstimulation, hallucinations, anxiety, weakness, and even the possibility of paralysis.

I do not know about you, but I think I will stick to natural ways instead of risking those effects.

There are plenty of other aphrodisiacs out there that you can use, but as it has been mentioned, science has not actually proven that using these methods is going to increase your sexual desire. But, it never hurts to try does it? Even though you may try aphrodisiacs, you need to be careful about what some of the side effects could be. Not all of them are going to be severe and permanently harm you. However, an allergic reaction can slow down the desire pretty fast if you do ask me!

No matter what you do, enjoy your love making and have fun getting there!

Chapter 6: The Importance Of Communication During Lovemaking

The Kama Sutra places a large amount of emphasis on the importance of communication during the love making process. The ancient text discusses the many different ways that couples have to communicate with one another as they explore each other's bodies in sensuous ways.

The different types of foreplay that we have discussed throughout this book are all great ways for couples to begin communicating to stimulate lovemaking.

It is important to ensure that both you and your partner are comfortable with keeping an open communication throughout the entire process of foreplay and lovemaking. Failing to ensure that you are both communicating can result in one of the partners being unhappy with the experience.

Having open communication is even more important than you and your partner have made the decision to try something new. Ensuring that you are both getting enjoyment out of what you are doing is important. If your partner is not enjoying what you are doing, showing them that you respect them enough to stop and try something different is a great way to build trust in the relationship.

The Kama Sutra says that sexual intercourse is about communication and pleasure. If a lack of communication is preventing you or your partner from having their needs met, it can lead to unnecessary tension and unhappiness between the couple.

There are some things that you do and do not want to talk about when you are making love. When you communicate with your partner physically as well as verbally, you will discover that you are going to have more pleasure.

1. Allow your hands to do the talking. Not all communication has to be verbal and sometimes the nonverbal communication is more powerful. Try and add in both verbal and nonverbal cues when you are making love with your partner. For example, you should have your partner draw circles around your palm with their finger. As they do this, tell them things that you like such as the pressure they are applying; but, also tell them one thing they should change like the direction they are going.

2. Do not ask your partner if they have come yet! When your partner comes, it is going to be quite obvious to you! When you ask about it, you are going to make your partner find that it is hard to reach their climax. If they are in the middle of it and you do not know if they are orgasming or not, then you are going to end up getting them to stop orgasming. If you do not know if your partner is reaching their end, ask your partner to give you some kind of signal when they are so that you know that you have successfully pushed them over the edge.

3. Show that you like what your partner is doing! Moan, squirm, scream if you can! Let your partner know that they have found something that you highly approve of and want it to happen more.

4. Do not say things like ew or gross. When you do not like something that your partner is doing, try and use more positive statements rather than yelling and ruining the mood. So, if your partner's tongue goes somewhere that you think is gross, try and tell them something else that you would like over what they are doing. Do not be too critical with your statements or you are going to end the mood before you are ready for it to. Not only that, but you are going to make your partner feel bad and then they may be less likely to have sexy time with you again anytime soon.

5. Experiment with dirty talk. Sometimes it can be frightening to use dirty talk because you are scared of sounding like an idiot or going too far with it. While this is a common fear, do not let it hold you back. If you or your partner goes too far with the dirty talk, then tell them about it. Quiet sex is not always a bad thing, but noise can make it to where your partner knows what you like.

6. Do not check your phone! Phones are part of everyday life. But, this does not mean that you have to get on it right after sex. Spend a little time with your partner so that they do not feel like it was just business. Only check your phone if you absolutely have to.

7. You have the power to say no. if you are not comfortable with what is going on, then you should not stay silent. Let your partner know right away. And, never feel like you are doing something wrong when you say no. You are doing the right thing and protecting yourself.

Chapter 7: The Embraces Of The Kama Sutra

Now that you have set the mood in your pleasure room, and you are well versed on what foods are most likely to increase arousal in you and your partner, you are ready to begin exploring the many different aspects of foreplay. In this chapter, we are going to have a look at the types of embraces the Kama Sutra lists.

When it comes to the art of love, embraces are very powerful. The embraces we are going to be listing here are not your everyday hug. The Kama Sutra identifies twelve embraces that typically occur naturally in relationships, but can also be used as foreplay.

The Embrace Of The Breasts – This embrace is going to be when the male presses his chest between the breasts of his woman This is the type of embrace that would take place later during foreplay.

The Embrace Of The Forehead – This is another incredibly personal embrace. It is the gesture of affection and makes two partners feel connected. This embrace occurs when one party touches three different parts of their body to the same parts on their lover.

The Embrace Of The Jaghana – This embrace includes some pain which is not for everyone. Some people find that this little bit of pain adds to their experience. This embrace occurs when a man presses the area known as the Jaghana on his lover. This area is found between a woman's thighs and her naval with his own body as he gets on top of her. after this has happened, the pain will be applied through the use of teeth or nails.

The Embrace Of the Thighs – This embrace occurs when one of the two partners forcibly presses one or both of their partner's thighs between their own.

The Milk And Water Embrace – This embrace is often interpreted as making love with your clothes on. It is when a woman and a man will hold each other like they were trying to merge their bodies together and become one.

The Piercing Embrace – This embrace occurs when a woman bends down as if to pick something up and "pierces" a man with her breasts. The man would then take hold of them.

The Pressing Embrace – This is when the male presses his partner's body forcibly against a wall. Pairing this embrace with a deep kiss is a sure way to get both partner's blood flowing fast.

The Rubbing Embrace – This embrace happens when two lovers are walking slowly together and rub their bodies against one another.

The Sesamum Seed And Rice Embrace – This embrace happens when two people are on a bed together and they are going to be tangled together so that it is hard to tell where one person ends and the other begins.

The Touching Embrace – This isn't so much an embrace as it is a soft touch from one partner to the other. This embrace is when one partner subtly touches his partner with his body as he goes in front of or alongside her.

The Tree Climbing Embrace – This embrace is when a woman places one foot to that of her man and the other to his thigh. After this has happened, she is then going to lock her arms behind his back and all while sounding like a bird.

The Twining Of A Creeper – This is when a female clings to her lover in a way similar to how a creeper wraps itself around a tree. She uses both her arms and her legs and lowers his face towards as if her lips are going to be placed on his. This is an embrace that would only happen in private.

The act of embracing is an important way for foreplay to begin. There are four different stages to embracing. For couples who are previously unknown to one another, embracing is a great way to remove the distance between them, whereas a couple who is familiar with one another may approach embracing with a drive.

The four different methods to embracing are listed next.

Touching – The partners begin to touch one another while they are talking.

Pulling – The distance between the partners is closed by pulling each other close.

Rubbing – The partners begin to caress and stroke one another.

Pressing Hard – The partner's press firmly against one another in anticipation for intercourse.

As well as embracing, massage is another important type of foreplay. Massage has the ability to make your partner feel cherished and relaxed; these feelings will lead to a greater enjoyment when the actual act of intercourse takes place.

Giving a massage is not a difficult thing to do, and there isn't really a right or wrong way to do it, as long as your partner is enjoying it. Here are some tips to help make your massage successful.

- Use a massage oil or lotion that is scenting in a smell that you and your partner both find appealing. While a massage oil is not necessary, a nice oil will make the massage even more sensual than not using one.

- Begin your massage at the top of your partner's body, at the head/neck area. Run your hands from the neck, just below the hairline, down to the shoulder area.

- Use long strokes going down your partner's back ending right above their butt.

- Keep your strokes firm, but not hard. This is intended to be a sensual massage, as opposed to a deep tissue massage.

- Using different amounts of pressure, alternate between long soothing strokes, and circular motions.

- Massage the arms, using long sweeping strokes from the shoulder to the end of the fingertips.

- Using the same technique as you used on the arms, massages the legs down to the feet.

Foreplay should never be rushed, every touch and caress are helping you and your partner learn more about one another and what you each like and dislike as well as what leads to your arousal.

Now that we have covered all of the embraces that are a part of the Kama Sutra, as well as how to use massage to your advantage, we are going to move on and cover the different types of kisses that are included in the Kama Sutra.

Chapter 8: The Kisses Of The Kama Sutra

When it comes to the aspect of kissing in the Kama Sutra, it is a very in depth topic. There are four different kinds of kissing as well as many different techniques.

The Types Of Kissing

There are four different types of kissing according to the Kama Sutra. Those four types include contracted, moderate, pressed, and soft. The type of kiss you are going to use is dependant on the part of the body you are kissing. We are going to cover each type of kiss, as well as when it should be used, below.

Contracted – You would use this type of kiss after you have crawled your nails across the skin of your partner. This type of kiss is firm and meant to distract your lover's skin from the feeling of your nail moving across.

Moderate – This is the type of kiss that is reserved for the cheeks, mouth, breasts, belly, and hips where there is an abundance of flesh, and you can sink your teeth in without causing any real pain. This is an urgent type of kiss that is forceful and lingers on the edge of causing pain.

Pressed – This type of kiss requires the use of the tongue to trace the curves of the body. It is a sensual kiss that is intended to make your partner quiver with desire.

Soft – This is the kind of kiss that is used where the limbs meet the body, as well as the breasts. The tongue is used to tease gently and is broken up with gentle nips of the teeth. This kiss is so gentle that it requires the focus of your partner to really feel it.

The Methods Of Kissing

As well as the four types of kissing, there are different methods of kissing that are laid out by the Kama Sutra. Kissing is easily one of the biggest aspects of foreplay, and the different techniques allow us to use our lips to communicate the depth of our desire to our partner.

The Clasping Kiss – This kiss occurs when a partner takes hold of his lover's lips between his own. One partner taking control over the other in this fashion can be extremely sensual.

Fighting Of The Tongue – When a woman performs The Clasping Kiss on her partner, and he responds bt thrusting his tongue into her mouth it is considered to be a battle of the tongues for control.

The Greatly Pressed Kiss – This kiss requires the giver to take her partner's lips between her fingers and touching her tongue to her lover's lips before she can fully kiss his lips.

The Kiss Of The Upper Lip – This is an intimate kiss that is performed when the male is going to focus on the female's upper lip as she is focusing on his lower lip. This kiss is meant to ignite passion within the couple.

The Kiss That Awakens – This is a kiss that is performed on a sleeping partner with the intention of waking them up. Typically this kiss would be given by someone who has returned home late at night.

The Kiss That Kindles Love – This is a kiss that happens when a person looks upon their lover with admeration and kisses various parts of their face to show their desire for their partner. While this kiss is not intended to wake the sleeping partner, it is thought that the sleeping partner will feel the desire of the awake partner in their dreams.

The Kiss That Turns Away – This is a kiss that is used during an argument of disagreement to draw a partner's attention away from what they are focused on. This kiss is forced upon one of the partner's in hopes of drawing their attention to the instigating partner instead of the issue at hand.

The Pressed Kiss – This kiss is a hard passionate kiss that is performed at the time that the lips of our lover are pressed to our lower lip. The force coupled with only kissing the lower lip leaves our partner wanting more.

The Stirring Kiss – This is a kiss that is performed by a woman in a warm and seductive manner. It is said that when done correctly this kiss can make a man who is not in the mood for sex become aroused.

The Throbbing Kiss – This kiss concentrates on kissing the lower lip of your partner and ignoring the upper lip. It is intended to make your partner want more.

The Touching Kiss – This kiss is used when lover's lips first touch. The giver gently caresses one the lips of her lover with the tip of her tongue and grasps the hand of her partner while keeping her eyes closed.

The Turned Kiss – This kiss takes place when the giver grabs his partners hand and gently turns her face towards him with his free hand, turning her into the kids. This is a kiss that we often see in movies and strikes us as romantic as the man is playing a role of sensitive and forceful.

Vatsyayana described the different ways of kissing and also warned that everyone responds to different kisses differently, which plays an important role in a relationship. Since kissing is the first step towards a sexually active relationship, it is essential that it is enjoyed by both partners. If it is not something that is enjoyed by both partners, it can cause an abrupt halt to the relationship. Due to the important of kissing in foreplay, it is essential that you pay attention to your partner's cues to help you determine what they do and do not like when it comes to kissing methods.

Chapter 9: Pressing, Marking, Scratching And Biting

Embracing and kissing aren't the only aspects of foreplay that the Kama Sutra covers. It also places emphasis on using your nails and teeth to bring pleasure to your partner.

Nails

Using your fingernails to press, mark and scratch your partner when the action is becoming intense is only acceptable in four different situations. Those four situations are:

- The first sexual interaction with a partner;

- When one partner is setting out on a journey;

- When one partner returns from a journey; and

- After the reconciliation of a fight.

It is important to make sure that your nails are clean and free of any sharp edges before you engage in the act of pressing, marking or scratching your partner.

While the list in the Kama Sutra is not all encompassing of all the different types of marks you can leave on your partner with your fingernails, the Kama Sutra covers eight different types of marks.

Circle – This is two half-moons that are impressed opposite of one another, typically on the navel, buttocks, or the joint of the thigh.

Half Moon – This mark is typically left on the neck or breasts and is in a curved shape.

Jump Of A Hare – This this symbol cis going to be placed near the nipple and is five marks all near one another.

Leaf Of A Blue Lotus – This mark is in the form of a leaf and is made of the breast or the hip.

Line – This mark is is a simple line that can be located anywhere the person wishes it to be.

Peacock's Foot – this is a mark made on the breast by all five nails. The mark has a curved appearance and takes a high level of skill to do correctly.

Sounding – This is when the nail is pressed hard enough on the partner's skin to make a sound, but this is done with no pain and thus no mark is going to be left as evidence on the body. This is typically done on the chin, breasts, lower lip, and jaghana.

Tiger's Claw – This mark is usually left on the breast and is in the shape of a curved line.
In the situation where one partner is leaving on a journey, it is common to make a mark on the thighs or breast of their lover as a token of remembrance. This mark is comprised of three or four lines all close to one another.

Teeth

Another form of sexual communication is through the act of biting. The Kama Sutra explained that biting fuels the heat of love and said that all kissing points, other then the eyes, upper lip, and tongue are suitable for biting as long as your partner is willing. While a whole chapter in the Kama Sutra is devoted to covering the act of biting, Vatsyayana cautioned against using the teeth to hurt your partner. Below we are going to cover some of the more common types of bites. Notice that none of the bites break the skin, although some so leave marks.

Hidden Bite – This bite is typically done by the man. It is traceable bu the red mark it leaves behind, but there are no other markings. It is usually done on the lower lip of the receiving individual.

Swollen Bite – In order to execute the swollen bite, the biting partner must press down on either side of the place they are going to bite. This causes the area that is going to be bitten to swell upwards. This is typically done to the lower lip of the receiving individual.

The Biting Of The Boar – This is a bunch of bites that are done around the shoulders in proximity to one another. These bites are only deep enough to leave impressions and redness and are meant to appear as if an animal has been feasting.

The Broken Cloud – This bite is done by a man on a woman and involves the man biting areas on the woman's breast leaving uneven marks that look like a cloud that has broken up.

The Coral And The Jewel – This bite is meant to be done on the throat, thighs and thighbones for maximum pleasure. It is when a bite is done with all of the teeth as well as the lips. The biter brings their teeth and their lips together during the bite, with the lips being thought of at the coral and the teeth being the jewel.

The Line Of Points – This is a technique where the biter bites multiple times, hard enough to leave a mark. The marks make a line. No skin in broken in this technique, only red marks are left behind. This is usually done on the thigh, armpit or neck.

The Point – This is usually done on the lower lip. The biter uses only their two front teeth leaving two red spots.
Biting should never be done with the intention of breaking the skin, and is meant to ignite a heightened desire between two partners. It is important to ensure that you have your partner's consent before engaging in any marking, whether it is from the teeth or the nails.

The central agenda of the Kama Sutra is to turn sexuality into eroticism, but Vatsyayana did point out that unchecked ferocity of desire can overwhelm the erotic pleasure and lead to a loss of humanity. Because of this, he stated that both parties should be on the same wave of sexual energy in order to avoid one of the partners from coming off as being too aggressive.

Chapter 10: Striking – Where To Strike, How To Strike And The Noises Made

Vatsyayana compared intercourse to having a quarrel. The reasons for this included in the parameters is because of those who tend to argue with it.. The Kama Sutra was very specific with how it approached the act of striking. There are places that are considered appropriate to hit, specific ways to hold the hand while hitting and even different sounds that are acceptable from the recipient of the hits.

Since some people find the act of striking during foreplay to be incredibly erotic, while others find it to be a turn-off, this is another time it is important to ensure you are communicating with your partner.

Striking is intending to come as a surprise and a shock to the person who is being hit. Since it is coming as a surprise, it stands to reason that the person being hit is going to cry out. There are eight different kinds of noises that were listed in the Kama Sutra as being appropriate to make.

- The sound Hin. This is a long sound that is similar to "in" but without the "n" sound at the end.

- A loud booming noise referred to as a thundering sound.

- A sound of enjoyment, similar to a kitten that is mewling or a cooing noise.

- A weeping sound that is similar to crying.

- The sound Phut, similar to the sound you hear when something is dropped in the water.

- The sound Phat, similar to the sound heard when bamboo is being split.

- The sound Plat, similar to the sound phat, but louder.

- The sound Sut, this is a sound made with the tongue clicking on the teeth.

There were other words and sounds that were listed in the Kama Sutra, though not in as much detail. Some of the words had a specific definitions like the words "mother" and "father", which are words forbiddance. There are also other words that are these sounds are going to be sounds of freedom as well as of the pain that one is feeling along with praise for what their partner is doing to them. There are also sounds that belong to animals that are occasionally made use of. The animals that are used include various forms of birds such as a parrot or sparrow.

As well as having specific noises that could be made, there were also specific places that were appropriate to hit:

- The shoulders;

- The head, but not the face;

- The space between the breast, but not the breast itself;

- The back,

- The jaghana, or middle part of the body; and

- The sides.

There were also four specific ways that were considered to be appropriate to hold the hand if you chose to strike your partner.

Striking With The Back Of The Hand – These hits are meant to be aimed at space between the breasts during the act of intercourse. This space should be hit will increase up until Congress has come to an end.

Striking With The Fingers Contracted – This hit is meant to be made by the man to the woman's head while he makes the sound Phat. The woman should reply with the cooing sound and the sound Phut.

Striking With The Fist – These hits are meant to be aimed at the back of the woman when she is sitting on the lap of the man. She should return these blows to the man, abusing him as if she were angry at him.

Striking With The Open Palm Of The Hand – These hits can be aimed at any of the appropriate parts of the body, but they aren't meant to cause physical pain to the recipient, rather they are intended to increase the physical pleasure the recipient is feeling.

Lovemaking and sex are an activity that we all participate in at some point or another. Being on the same page as your partner regarding what you both enjoy as well as what you both consider being appropriate is an important aspect of learning what you are both going to enjoy. Striking can be something that adds depth to your lovemaking experience, as long as it is done correctly.

Chapter 11: The Basic Sex Positions

The Kama Sutra covered many different sex positions in addition to all of the aspects of foreplay we have already covered. Since the sex positions aren't the primary emphasis of the Kama Sutra, we aren't going to go too in-depth about the positions and instead, we are just going to cover some of the basic positions.

The Clasping Position – This is a position that happens when both the male and the female stretch their legs out over one another during intercourse.

The Erotic V Position – This position requires some flexibility and is accomplished when the woman is sitting on the edge of a table, and the man stands in front of her. The man may be required to bend his legs to bring himself to the height of the woman.

The Pressing Position – This begins as the Clasping Position that we saw above, and becomes the Pressing Position when intercourse begins, and the woman presses into her lover with her thighs.

The Rising Position - This position is achieved when the woman raises both of her thighs straight up in order to make herself more accessible for penetration.

The Splitting Bamboo Position – This position is when a woman places one leg over her lover's shoulder and then alternates which leg is up on the shoulder.

The Yawning Position – This position takes place when a woman raises her thighs and keeps them apart during intercourse.

Sammukha: the female is going to lean back against a wall with her legs spread. The male will then enter her. If you are a shorter female, you may discover that standing on something will make this position a little easier. Because of the contact, this position is very intimate and even offers for deeper penetration.

Janukurpara: you will need to be strong to do this position, so before you do it, you may find that you want to go to the gym some and get used to lifting some weight. As the male, you will lift up your female and lock your elbows just under her knees. Your hands are going to be on her butt and she is going to wrap her arms around your neck to help with the support.

Piditaka: you do not have to include acrobats in your sex life to make it thrilling. With this position, you are going to have your female lay on her back and bring her knees up to her chest. You are going to kneel in front of her and spread her thighs while giving her a little extra support by placing her hips on your thighs. From this position your female is going to feel as if she is tighter than normal being that her vagina is going to be more narrowed thanks to her legs being up. If you want to increase the pressure, have her cross her ankles or even bring her legs together more.

Virsha: in essence, this is just the reverse cowgirl. Just like the position is done with that name, you are going to have the female on top and she is going to impale herself upon his manhood with her back to him. She needs to be strong enough to hold herself up while you are flat on your back. While she rides you, you should enjoy the view!

Tripadam: if you are looking for a good position for a quicky, you are going to want to use this postion. You will both be standing and facing each other. She is going to bring one knee up to your hip and you are going to grab her leg just beneath her knee. Form here you are going to enter her and enjoy your fun!

Rocking horse: with the male sitting cross legged somewhere, he is going to support himself with his hands while the female sits on his lap and grinds her pelvis into his until he is inside of her. Once he is inside of her, the female is going to be able to rock back and forth until both of you orgasm.

Glowing triangle: first you will start out in the missionary position. After you have penetrated her, the male will get up on all fours, bringing the female's butt with her and applying pressure to her feet. The male is going to stay still once more while the female rolls her hips and brings both of them over the edge.

Nirvana: the female is going to lay on her back and stretch her legs out while the male gets on top of her and keeps her thighs on the outside of hers while penetrating her. There is going to be a lot of friction between the two and the male is going to do all of the work.

Ballerina: this position is much like a spooning position and it is extremely intimate being that your partner will be cradling you the entire time. To perform this act, you will lay beside him and lift whichever leg is on top so that he can get his legs in between yours. Being that he is behind you, you can bring your leg back to rest on his as he enters you and makes love to you.

Curled angel: as the female, you will lay on your side and curl your knees up so that they are touching your breasts. The male will then get behind the female and penetrate her from behind. The male and female are going to be close thus making this a romantic position. In order to bring more friction between the two, she can press her knees together more so that it narrows her vagina more.

Double decker: having the male lay on his back, the female is going to ease him into her before turning so she is not facing him. Now resting on her elbows, the female will be half laying on her partner and rocking his world.

The seduction: have the female on her back and bring her knees in. The male will get on top and enter her vagina. After that, she will move back and forth in what appears to be circles. This position also makes it to where the clit can be stimulated as well as other sensitive parts of the male's body.

Crouching tiger: getting on all fours, the male is going to stand behind his female and enter her. keeping her knees together is going to increase the love making.

Of course, this is just a brief overview of some of the positions that are in the Kama Sutra. The Kama Sutra goes much further into depth regarding the positions that are available for you to try. While it is not all inclusive, it is a great starting point if you are looking for new positions for you and your partner to try.

You can be as creative as you would like to work towards creating a positive atmosphere when you are in bed with your partner. You can use the positions above as a guide to see how limitless you can truly be when it comes to the position you are in when you engage in intercourse.

Conclusion

Now that you have gone through this book, you should have a good idea of the origin of the Kama Sutra and what it was intended for. It was not intended to be just a guide to the positions you can use to engage in intercourse; it was a guide to how to learn what you find to be pleasurable in your life and your relationships.

In its entirety, the Kama Sutra can help you to understand and decipher your desires and beliefs while also introducing you to a culture that is historically known for their sexual beliefs and practices.

This book has covered many of the different aspects of foreplay as they are listed out in the Kama Sutra. You have been advised on the different types of embracing, hitting, biting, marking and embracing. All of these things can help bring you and your partner closer. As you build on the connection you have with your partner; you are going to find that you begin to experience more happiness in other aspects of your life as well.

I hope that reading this book has helped you to learn more about yourself and has inspired you to share the wealth of knowledge you have received with your partner and use that information to your advantage.

Tantric Sex

Introduction Handbook To Tantra

Introduction

The meaning of 'tantra' conjures up a myriad range of teachings, philosophies, and meanings and there will always be a huge debate when people discuss this rather esoteric topic. There will be people agreeing with some aspects of what you see and there will be people disagreeing with you strongly. Yet, you must know that the actual term 'tantra' signifies something very meaningful.

To understand the meaning of this word, we would have to start with another Indian word called 'sutra.' Sutras were critical texts of Hinduism, Jainism, and Buddhism. The sutra that gained maximum fame in the Western World is, perhaps, the Kama Sutra which is a text that talks in detail about erotic and sexual arts. By the way, this sutra is in no way connected to Tantra. Another equally famous sutra is that of Patanjali called the Yoga Sutra.

Let us start again with the word, sutra, whose literal meaning is 'thread' and refers to a particular thread or line of thought. Some believe that this 'thread' refers to the physical threads that bind the text together.

So, the sutra is a single thread of thought and tantra is an entire system of thought. The Sanskrit meaning of 'tantra' is 'loom.' We are not just talking about the cloth that is woven with the threads, but the entire machinery on which the piece of cloth is made. Originally, sutras came in the form of books, whereas tantras were taught by the guru or teacher directly to his disciples or students. Soon, considering the highly literate society that this part of society was, the oral teachings also took the form of books, notes, summaries, etc.

Now, let us come to the 6th century in Europe. During this time, the Roman Empire was in tatters and there was absolutely no stability leading to the increased growth of warfare and petty battles amongst smaller warlords. The worst affected aspects of society were education and knowledge which had reached abysmal depths and illiteracy and ignorance was rampant in Europe.

The Eastern society, particularly India, was on a path of stability and growth. Education and intellectual thinking were on the rise in this entire nation. Kashmir, specifically became a melting pot of cultures and yet, ancient worship rituals and traditions still existed here; especially the worship of Siva and Shakti; more on this in the next chapter.

Here, the word 'tantra' or loom has been given another connotation; that of weaving together Siva, the representative of consciousness, with Shakti, the representative of power. Also, the loom could be the weaving together of Siva, Shakti, and other 'sutras' or threads of Vedic tradition and culture. At this time in the Kashmir valley, Jainism and Buddhism were also thriving and some aspects of those religions always began to be woven together to combine Siva and Shakti to create a new form of thought or 'Tantra.'

This is just the beginning of Tantra. Read on for more.

Chapter One: History and Origins of Tantra

Now, that you know the basic etymology of 'sutra' and 'Tantra' let us dive right in and get more information as to the origins and the history of this rather misunderstood and misinterpreted system of thought. Tantra can be believed to be the weaving of the 'sutras' of Siva and that of Shakti to achieve the divine and transcend beyond human senses.

There were multiple oral traditions that were imbibed into the Tantra of weaving together of Siva and Shakti. These traditions were most likely derived from Dravidian matriarchal societies that honored and respected the female aspect of life. In these traditions, women were very powerful influencers and great teachers too.

There were highly powerful and meaningful rituals to mark transition points. These rituals were all centered upon nature and were very important connecting lines to nature. Most importantly, these female-oriented traditions rarely separated these rituals from routine life. They did not have priestly class or any kind of monastic order which controlled the other parts of the society or tradition.

These teachings or the Tantra thoughts found a lot of popularity among the burgeoning middle class in India, which was becoming wealthier and more powerful than before the time we are talking about (around the 6th century). This emerging middle class was more or less unaffected by the caste-consciousness of the Vedic nature and also by the monastic male-dominated Buddhist philosophy of the times.

Additionally, these shamanic-like traditions taught that enlightenment was possible right here, right now. These traditions were practical and easy to follow unlike the scholarly and monastic teachings of the conventional religions in force at that time. These traditions were very immediate and very vibrant too.

The immediacy of the outcomes was very attractive as people did not have the compulsion to wait for reincarnations and rebirths for salvation. Divinity was not described in any abstract and distant form consisting of a collection of confusing deities. On the other hand, divinity was explained as something that is all-pervasive and that which each of us is a part of. In fact, divinity is not something that we are a part of, but it was the whole of the Universe.

Nothingness, as described in Buddhism, this was not an easy concept to understand for the average person. The concept of nothingness was changed into a form that was easier to interpret and comprehend; that nothingness became an all-pervading, omnipresent, and universal consciousness.

The physical world which was considered a deception to the traditional view became an illusion in this middle-class accepted new tradition. Everything and everyone in this universe became a differently projected part of the universal consciousness. As we get better at understanding, the awareness of the non-duality concept, we slowly began to understand the illusionary aspect of what our five senses project to us until finally, we can now visualize and accept the entire Universe including us, the world around us, and the Divine, as one and the same.

All these teachings together were referred to as Tantra and continued through the entire Classical Era, which lasted for about 400-500 years. Multiple individual and independent teachers created many lineages that had among them a few diversities but mostly commonalities.

Kashmir Shaivism was one such lineage created and remained highly prevalent for a few centuries. However, the Tantra lineage highly influenced both the then prevalent Hinduism and Buddhism. The Hinduism as we know it today is particularly influenced by the Tantra tradition. Buddhism created an entirely new sub-sect called Vajrayana Buddhism that still survives in the Himalayas even today.

Therefore, Tantra was viewed as a spiritual science by many independent practitioners. They believed this science was available for adaptation to one's set of beliefs. It is free of any one particular religious dogma or principles and instead, drew commonalities from all.

Irrespective of who created a particular Tantra sub-sect (for want of a better word), the following commonalities were found across these different types:

- Direct relationship between the gurus (teachers) to the disciples (students)
- Mindfulness in all aspects
- Rituals were used to increase awareness
- All arbitrary rules of culture and religion were rejected
- Acceptance of followers irrespective of caste, gender, nationality, language, etc.

- Unmitigated access to participating in the rituals connecting to the divine
- Belief in the body sensations including sexual experiences as a path that will lead to the divine; it is important not to replace this path of sensual pleasures to reach the divine as a distraction

While sexuality and sensuality are debated on their importance by people from different belief systems, the fact that sexual experiences are part and parcel of the means of achieving the divine in Tantra philosophy is irrefutable. While some manuals choose the union of male and female energies through the sexual practice to attempt to meet the divine energy, there are other cases in evidence wherein tantra practitioners including established gurus of those times were imprisoned and branded for using licentious behavior to corrupt the priestly Brahmin class.

While the extant texts are not very vocal on the points of sexual union and sexual pleasure, there is no doubt that the texts were written by highly learned scholars of those times who were well-versed and practiced in the Tantric systems and rituals. Additionally, many of these scholars chose to keep the secrets of direct transmission of energy highly 'secretive' as it was ordered by their own teachers to do so. What happened behind the 'veils' can only be surmised and speculated and not really known except by the ones who had achieved the capability to know and experience the outcome of the direct transmission.

Art and Architecture

While the texts remain inconclusive about the use of sexual practices, the art and architecture that exist even today are highly illustrative and leave no doubt in the minds of the modern man to the use of sex in Tantra philosophy. The sculptors and temple architecture are replete with vivid and potent imagery of the union of female (yoni) with the male (lingam) genitals through the act of sex.

The female yoni consists of the vulva and the vagina and the male lingam is representative of the penis. The imagery of the male and female deities are shown locked in carnal embraces. Most of the tantra illustrations present the consort and the practitioner in sexual union pose. Here it is important to note that the male is usually taken to be the practitioner and the female is the consort. However, in truth, Tantra philosophy treats both equally and both could be practitioners and consorts in turn. Many of the great teachers were women while many of the writers of texts were male.

Disappearance of Tantra

The classical form of tantra more or less disappeared around the 1100s when Islam took its roots in India. Buddhism almost completely disappeared and tantric rituals and practices were also mostly forgotten. Yet, three forms of Tantra continued to survive and does even to this day and the three forms include:

1. Hatha Yoga – this lineage of Tantra retains and preserves the practical rituals and teachings including and, specifically, the embodiment of mindfulness practices; however without much philosophical depth
2. Vajrayana Buddhism – retained the original rituals and texts along with the philosophical teachings around Buddhism
3. The Sri Vidya lineage through Brahmanism – this lineage completing removed and cleared all the rule-

rejecting aspects of tantra and became sanitized under the approval of Brahmanism and Vedic context

Tantra in the Contemporary Age

The largely forgotten Tantra philosophy came to the fore again nearly 800-900 years later in Europe. This rediscovered format is replete with the original vibrancy and diversity that existed during its primary days around the 5th century. The reason for this comeback is easy to understand, and here's why and how it happened:

Even before connecting with India, Nepal, and other Eastern cultures, European spirituality already had an element of secret sexual traditions that were considered sacred. When the minds of these eastern and western secret sex-based philosophies met, the resurgence of tantra happened. The modern tantra came alive combining elements of the classical tantric texts of India along with the western sexual mysticism creating a new kind of amalgamated, reconstituted, and reformulated thought. The contemporary tantra system incorporates the elements of breathing techniques, energy flow, and mindfulness to bring alive the spirit of the passionate divine. And thus, Tantra was reborn in its present avatar.

Even today, some teachers and schools are aligned to the Kashmir Shaivism lineage and teach and propagate rituals and teachings from this school. Many others are promoting Vajrayana Buddhism that is simplified and made more adaptable in the Western way of life. Even teachers and followers of the Sri Vidya lineage are rediscovering and reconnecting with the sexual dimensions of their tantra and are redesigning concepts to include these elements as well.

Osho or Bhagwan Shree Rajneesh founded a Tantra school of thought based on his own understanding and interpretations of the tantric systems. In fact, his teachings reached far and wide across the globe and gave rise to a new word called, 'neotantra.' David Deida also used tantric principles initially to set up his own teaching school.

Many of the contemporary teachings use the performance of sex as the center for achieving divinity and it plays a very important role and forms the foundations of the modern tantric schools. Yet others do reject 'sexuality' completely from their teachings. Again, if you removed the sexual aspect and prominence of the sexual act from these contemporary tantric teachings, you will find the same common threads that we found when we studied diverging tantra schools that opened in the 5th century in India. These commonalities include:

- Personal and enlightened transmissions directly from teacher to student; it is important (just like old times) to have a spiritually gifted teacher
- Practice of mindfulness
- The importance of ritual
- Open to all irrespective of caste, creed, race, gender, language, nationality, etc.
- Teachings that promise direct access to the divine and related experiences

More in the Western Form of Tantra

There are four forms of tantra that are popular in the Western world today and they include:

White Tantra – This is an esoteric form of tantra practiced using sexual energy as the foundation while leveraging on the power of meditation, visualization, and control of breath to seek divine enlightenment. This is usually practiced alone by an individual.

Red Tantra – This includes the principles of White Tantra along with using sexual techniques on and with another partner in play

Pink Tantra – This is the most popular tantra system that is in use in the West and includes the principles, rituals, and practices of the White and the Red Tantra. It is focused on relationships between couples and uses devotional energy through the heart for solving relationship problems and issues.

Black Tantra – Almost out of favor today, this format employs sexual energies to change things in people outside of the practitioners and usually comes with an intention to harm others.

Role of Women in Tantra

In tantric traditions, a woman has been accorded as having a higher spiritual attitude than a man driven by a higher intensity in the following elements as compared to a man:

- Her frame
- Her emotions
- Her psychic evolution

Therefore, as per tantric traditions, it is believed that achieving enlightenment through the awakening of the Kundalini Shakti is easier in a woman's body than a man's. Another reason for this belief is the idea that when a man achieves a higher plane of consciousness and comes back to this plane after that experience, he is not able to bring back some of those experiences to this realm whereas a woman can do this.

When a man goes deep into his consciousness and then returns to gross awareness, a kind of a veil seems to fall in between the two planes for him. However, for a woman, this veil does not fall leaving the experiences from the higher consciousness to be brought into the gross consciousness.

Additionally, a woman's state of awareness is spiritually charged and this charge is reflected even in the gross life in the form of that tender look, feelings of sympathy and understanding for others' pains, etc. In fact, many tantric practitioners are of the opinion that in the absence of women, this world will become a desert with nothing but the stark surroundings; no color, no love, no passion, etc.

In Kundalini yoga, the mooladhara chakra in a man is located in a very congested area with little or no physical access. On the other hand, the mooladhara chakra of a woman is easily accessible and even be touched and activated easily. This makes it very easy for the awakening of the spirits in a woman's body than a man's which is why the woman is often given a higher spiritual place than a man in tantric systems.

The woman has always been the energy transporter whereas the man has always been the medium. This woman who helps in transportation a man's energy need not be a wife only. She could be a daughter, a disciple, or a mother. Mary was the mother of Jesus Christ whereas the Mother in the Aurobindo Ashram was a disciple.

Tantric traditions worship the woman as a goddess. There are 64 yoginis, who are the female gender of yogis. Shakti is the creator and Siva is the instrument. Without Shakti, Siva cannot create and in all Tantric systems, this belief of the union of man and woman needed for evolution and progress is many times misinterpreted as mere sexual pleasure.

In summary, from an Eastern viewpoint, Tantra is not relegated to getting heightened sexual pleasure or finding an improved way of having sex but is a way of life in which you use everyday experiences of the world (including sex) and convert them into divine experiences. Tantra teaches that you do not need to withdraw from worldly things to achieve divine enlightenment, but if you focus your energies mindfully on the routine day-to-day activities of life, you can get divine enlightenment because everything in this universe is part of the divine.

In the Western world, sadly, Tantra has been relegated to a practice that consists of esoteric sex out of the reach of people who don't understand it. In fact, there are multiple schools that market Tantra sex as a solution for sexual dysfunctions and problems ranging from boredom to other severe issues. Well, Tantra is more than this. It is a way of life and incorporating the practices consistently will help you lead a more fulfilled and understanding life than before.

All spiritual paths are always undertaken along with a woman for company. Similarly, a woman cannot undertake a spiritual path successfully without a man and so the equality of man and woman comes into play. One cannot survive without the other. In fact, there is a famous portrait of Shiva that is represented as one-half male and the other half as female which is what Tantra is all about; the combining of the female and male energies to achieve divine enlightenment.

Chapter Two: Benefits of Following Tantra Practices

While there is a common misconception in the Western world about Tantra being only a system to increase sexual pleasure, the previous chapter, I hope, has helped you understand that this wonderful system goes beyond mere sexuality. This chapter is, therefore, dedicated to giving you the benefits of practicing tantric traditions. There are multiple elements in Tantra teachings that in the growth and development of an individual spiritual journey and his or her physical health. Let's look at some of them.

Before we go there, there is one more word of caution. The tantric texts are written in a difficult language using codes and formats that are not easy for an average person to read and interpret correctly. It is precisely for this reason that there are so many fraudulent schools spreading the wrong kind of information about this ancient and valuable belief system. The first thing to do is to become associated with a school that is authentic and reputable so that you can get all the benefits of a direct guru-disciple relationship.

Tantra is actually a system to help you achieve a higher plane of consciousness, referred to as Samadhi. The use of sex is only an instrument to achieve this Samadhi state. The actual act of sex is designed to take you beyond carnal pleasures that are limited to human senses. While the pleasure aspect of sex is also heightened through the use of tantric practices, these practices are also helpful in improving your physical and spiritual health.

There are usually two paths of Tantric practices that are used; the left-hand path and the right-hand path. For the average person, the left-hand path is considered most appropriate as it helps in achieving tantric enlightenment without sacrificing sexual pleasure. The right-hand path is more for the highly advanced practitioner and may not suit the needs of the average beginner. The processes in the right-hand path focus on intense meditative and symbolic techniques connected to sexual energy but without participating in the actual sexual act itself. Both these paths are 'correct' and it is not possible to say which is better than the other.

Tantra principles are based on a presumption that sexual energy comes from the base chakras including:

- Mooladhara chakra
- Svadhisthana chakra
- Manipura chakra

All the above chakras are located either at the navel level or below it. This sexual energy originating from the base chakras can be moved up to the upper chakras which are:

- Anahata or the heart chakra
- Visuddha or the throat chakra
- Anja or the third eye chakra
- Sahasrara or the crown chakra

The deliberate movement of the sexual energy from the base chakras to the upper chakras through tantric practices and rituals is designed to enhance both sexual and spiritual experience for the practitioners. The benefits include more fulfilling and more sustaining outcomes of both the sexual and spiritual experiences than before.

The tantric practices not only gives enhanced and the ultimate sexual pleasure that all of us strive to achieve but also benefits our physical and spiritual growth. The tantric practices, if done correctly and as per set norms, will help in producing sensations of bliss through love and sexual union from the human perspective and also from the perspective of joining the male and female energies through the act.

In the commonly practiced sexual encounters, most of the participants voice a sense of dissatisfaction and incompletion from the act in addition to feeling exhausted after reaching sexual peaks. This rather debilitating feeling of exhaustion is not just temporary but can easily spill over into other aspects of your emotional and physical life leaving you tired and fatigued more often than you'd like.

The loss of life energy or prana is bound to lead to health imbalances that can ultimately lead you to not enjoy the act at all. Using a few asanas, yoga postures, and some techniques from the teachings of Tantra, it is possible for a couple to preserve sexual energy and direct it upwards making sure every cell in the body is awakened through these practices.

For example, there is a technique referred to as transfiguration in tantra in which a couple sit in front of each other (fully clothed) without any physical contact and gaze into each other's eyes. It is important not to reduce this technique to a mere staring exercise. This tantric exercise requires you to be with your partner in a very intimate and profound way. By following this practice diligently, you will notice that there will come a time when both of you can see a personality beyond the eyes.

Each of you will see a certain beauty in the other that is impossible to ignore, reject or hate. Finding this almost pure enigma in each other will create a kind of love in the relationship that will go beyond human expectations and requirements from the each other allowing for free love to flow between the partners resulting in a deeper and more connected relationship.

Here are some of the physical benefits reported by practitioners of Tantra-based techniques driven by increased and seamless energy flow through the bloodstream into every nook and corner of the body:

- Improved toning of muscles
- Rejuvenated and revitalized skin texture leading to improved complexion
- Reduced movement of the spinal cord and slow back pain
- Reduction in fat deposits
- Release of toxins from the body
- Maintenance of youthful energy and looks along with improved physical vitality
- Reduction in wrinkles
- Firmer breasts
- Toning of muscles in the hip and the abdomen resulting in a flatter tummy and improved gait quality
- Calf muscles were highly regenerated
- A sustained sense of joy and happiness
- Reduction in menstrual secretions along with reduced premenstrual symptoms

Men practitioners also reported increased benefits from the preservation and redirection of sexual energy resulting in a healthier body and improved creative energy flow throughout the system. Tantra practices encourage the consumption of a low-protein macrobiotic diet that has a balanced amount of yin and yang to match the feminine and masculine balance resulting from following tantric practices.

Women practitioners are highly benefited as well as Tantra practices help in building and improving overall general health by channelizing the preserved energy right through the body. Tantra techniques help to calm the body and mind while improving energy levels. Practicing tantra techniques is a way for people to retreat themselves from this mad, hectic world and re-energize their body and mind. Especially, through the regular practice of Tantra yoga asanas which call for steady and slow movements of the body moving from one asana to another seamlessly. The conscious breathing done during this time is always a method to calm down your mind.

More Benefits of Practicing Tantra

In addition to the general benefits mentioned above, tantra yoga is known to benefit by helping people deal with the following conditions by taking advantage of increased energy levels in the body:

- Stiffness in the body
- Stress and anxiety
- General fatigue
- Shoulder and back problems

While enlightenment may not happen overnight by Tantra practices (as it is not some kind of flashy miracle operation), sustained efforts at getting the right techniques and performing them patiently will go a long way in improving your spiritual and physical well-being. Of course, a healthy body is a prerequisite to achieve awakened states of consciousness and this theory is valid for all the systems present in this world. Healthy eating combined with a healthy lifestyle is critical to ensuring the successful outcome of any holistic healing system.

Chapter Three: Tantra Techniques

While practicing tantra techniques as a couple is available in plenty, there are multiple techniques that you can use as an individual without a partner to improve your sexual, physical, and spiritual health. Here are some such techniques that you can practice alone:

Connecting With Your Core

First, rub your palms together, so they become warm. Then, place one palm over your heart and the other palm over your genitals. Don't play or rub your chest or your genitals. Simply place your warmed palms there. Now, focus and feel the energies from these two primary energy centers radiating into your palms. Focus on this radiating energy and breathe deeply.

Imagine a circuitry that connects these two core energy centers in your body. Breathe and feel the heat transferring in the circuit between the two centers. Take a break. Again, breathe and feel the energy passing through the connected circuitry.

With sustained practice, you will be able to feel the energy flowing between these two centers more easily and more intensely than before. This energy flow is the core of your being and being aware of it will help you understand and draw from this energy.

Squeezing Your Pelvic Muscles

In this exercise, squeeze the muscles near the place from where you pass urine in a way that mimics holding on to the desire to pee. Squeeze for a short count of up to 5 and then relax these muscles. Repeat the squeezing and relaxing processes. This technique which comes under the umbrella of Kegel exercises is referred to as pelvic floor squeeze. One squeeze and one relaxation form one set of pelvic floor squeeze exercise.

The important point to note here is that you must squeeze in such a way to understand how you feel internally rather than to hold your breath and have an external effect because of the squeeze. Again, the tightness of your squeeze is irrelevant. You must simply focus on your sensations as you squeeze and relax these muscles.

Sustained repetition every day improves the strength of these muscles and it is possible to release and use your sexual energies by performing these pelvic floor squeeze exercises.

Tilt and Tuck

If you have seen any pornographic films or even the usual films where the sexual act is shown, you will notice that the partners use a thrusting motion during the act wherein they move back and forth with their hips. Perhaps, many of us still use this technique even in our lives. While this may look nice for the watchers, in truth, this technique is not very pleasurable for the partners.

The better option is to bend your knees and imagine your pelvis to be a bowl (like a salad bowl) and rock it. A good analogy would be the movement of belly dancers. Try to mimic their hip movements. Start slowly and with diligent practice; you will find it easier to do the tilt and tuck motion and have more pleasure in your sexual act than with the trusting kind of motion. This tilt and tuck movement that you practice is a great way to activate the latent sexual energy at the base of your spine

Abdominal Breathing

Most of us take breathing for granted. We simply don't understand or, rather, refuse to value its utmost importance to our lives. Except for some powerful swimmers and other sportsmen, for the average man, it is nearly impossible to remain without breathing for more than a minute. The maximum time for humans to be able to remain alive without breathing is 3 minutes. And yet, we take this divine activity for granted despite knowing that if we didn't breathe, we are dead!

So, focusing on your breath is one of the first techniques taught in any of the eastern traditions. An easy breathing technique used in tantra is abdominal breathing. Place your palm on your stomach and endeavor to breathe from there. It is very likely that breathing in this way makes you deliberately take bigger breaths than otherwise and you are bound to feel more connected to yourself too. Focusing on our breathing helps us to focus on our bodies and the movements that take place with each breath and nearly all tantra techniques are based on connecting with your body either by yourself or with your partner.

As you keep practicing, you will notice that it becomes easy to move from your headspace to your body space with just one breath.

Practice Making Sounds

Many of us who practice masturbation feel ashamed or guilty about it and for fear of being caught in the act, we choose not to make sounds. Yes, masturbation is not really an approved sexual act in Tantra philosophy. Yet, there are times when our desire gets the better of us and we give in, right? Making articulate and sensual sounds can activate sexual energy in a much nicer way than otherwise.

Try making suitable sounds the next time and you will notice that the pleasure becomes magnified. Practice making sounds without actually masturbating or while you are doing something pleasurable such eating a succulent piece of fruit or a fabulously sweet dessert so that you can include them in your future lovemaking sessions with your partner.

Treat Lovemaking as a Sacred Ritual

Any change first needs to take place in your mind. Shift your perspective from 'having sex' with your partner to 'making love' to your partner and performing something that will help you reach out to the divine. Set up your bedroom in the form of an altar. Put things that are special and important and connect to both of you; things that have brought both of you together, etc. Place special photos and clicks of special moments in strategic places.

Arrange sacred books that both of you enjoy reading. You can also place scared mementos like crystals and gemstones that have the power to enhance the love between the two of you; or, perhaps, help in the healing of wounds that cropped up between the two of you. Before the lovemaking session, light fragrant candles, incense, and create a wonderfully sensual and nurturing scene. Of course, it is important not to overpower the place with excessive fragrance. Use your creativity and do things that both of you can appreciate.

Meditate Before the Lovemaking Session

Meditation before the session creates the right intent for the lovemaking. Take things gradually. First, sit in front of each other and meditate together looking into each other's eyes with love and passionate intent. In your mind, call upon your favorite deity and offer her or him your body. Visualize a ball of love and sexual energy surrounding each of you individually and one that combines this energy that envelopes both of you together.

Set intentions in place in your respective minds as to what you want to give in this lovemaking session. Talk to your partner and spell out your joint intentions. Such discussions can enhance the love and sexual energy between the two of you while creating a beautiful sense of transparency and togetherness that will only make this relationship more beautiful and stronger than before.

Be 100% Present throughout the Session

It is important that for any relationship to nurture and get better that each partner commits herself or himself to be 100% (completely immersed) in the relationship. The same holds good even in each lovemaking session that you promise to each other. Committing ourselves to being present in the moment physically, emotionally, and spiritually has the power to take the lovemaking session to a different level where honesty, true feelings, and vulnerability also come into play.

This scenario will help both of you to delve deep into yourselves and into each other as you find new sources of sexual energy coursing through your body even before you begin the physical lovemaking session. Honesty is a very important attitude to have in Tantra. Being honest about how you feel at the moment and talking about it will create a clear pathway that you can traverse to reach your partner and vice versa.

Keep checking with your body sensations and do not be in denial. For example, for women, if your yoni is not yet wet, then it means you are not ready and fully committed to receiving. It is important not to go against your natural responses and pretend to something that doesn't exist. Tell your partner you need more time, or perhaps, more foreplay.

Instead of pretensions, keep digging deep into yourself and look for blockages, resistances, and barriers that are preventing you from being 100% present there with your partner.

Practice Tantric Massages on Each Other

Again, take time off before the actual lovemaking session and enjoy and worship each other's body. Be fully present and conscious of every aspect of yours and your partner's body so that when the time comes, there is a perfect union. Avoid rushing into the act. Instead, continue to build up your passions because this is not mere sex but something that will help you connect with the divine. So, focus, take things slowly and enjoy every moment.

Massages are great ways to feel and enjoy each other's touch. Touching is not always a representative of erotic passion. Unbridled love can be expressed in the form of a warm hug that will set your partner's heart aflutter. However, massages done before a lovemaking session are designed to merge body and mind of the two partners.

The emphasis on tantric massage (or conscious touch) is on the receiver and not the giver of the massage. Both are mindfully involved in the process. Mindful massaging alights and keeps the flame of love and desire burning and burning long after the session is over. The best thing about conscious is that it is very easy and yet, unfortunately, not used by many couples. Here are a few tips:

First, decide the basics – This simply means who will receive and who will give. You could take turns to do the receiving and giving. However, it is not possible to receive and give simultaneously with full awareness because it is easy to get lost between the two. The receiver will sit or lie down in a comfortable position with eyes closed. The giver should find a convenient position to place himself or herself conveniently close to the receiver.

Synchronize your breathing – Breathing together is a critical aspect of connected lovemaking. Synchronize your breathing by observing the receiver's breathing. It is usually the giver who matches his or her breathing to that of the receiver. This is a way of telling the receiver that you as a giver are holding the space for him or her. This step is bound to take some time as both the partners will have to get into their natural breathing rhythm and yet, find the way to synchronize with the other and relax in the entire process.

Be aware of how you are feeling – Focus on your own feeling and be totally aware of the state of mind you are in at that point in time. Do not judge your feelings or your body sensations. Simply observe the feeling. This should be done by both the receiver and giver. When you are acutely aware of yourself at any moment in time, it is easy to pass on this sense of mindfulness and awareness to your partner as well. When both the partners do it in harmony, there is bound to be sensations that resonate with each other.

Make sure your intent to give reflects in your touch – the True intention is the biggest motivation to get things done in an intended way. When you are massaging, make sure your intention to give unconditionally is reflected in your touch. The receiver could make a request as to where and how he or she wants the touch to take place. The giver should then put his or her full intent to giving what the receiver requested.

Literally, touch from your heart – Start the touch connection from your heart, literally. Ideally, the giver should place his or her hand over the receiver's heart by first placing the palm followed by the fingers. This position will ensure that the hearts of the receiver and the giver are directly connected through the left arm of the giver. This position literally connects the partners at their hearts.

Again, check if your breathing is synchronized and for a moment, feel the heart of your receiving partner beating on your palm. Now, place the right hand at the point where the massage needs to be given. Again, place the palm first so that there is stability in the hold. At this point, the receivers must mindfully feel the palm of the giver on the agreed body position and open his or her heart to receive the conscious touch. Stay connected like this for as long as you want and feel your hearts connected. This can be a very humbling moment as heart-to-heart connects have the power to create humility in a relationship.

Enjoy the massaging mindfully and together – Now, slowly move your hands through the receiver's body while being mindfully aware that your breath and your palms on your hearts are grounding both of you. Ask the receiver to 'actively' enjoy the massage through use of gentle sighs and pleasurable sounds. This will help the receiver to be mindfully aware of the giver's touch instead of allowing his or her mind to go off on its own path. Givers should follow their instincts for the right kind of pressure and direction to take in the massaging process. There could be added connection if eye contact can be maintained between the giver and the receiver.

Finally, trust your ability to give and receive love – Trust your body's ability to give and receive pleasure and by doing this, you are facilitating a deeper communicative connection with your partner that goes beyond words. Avoid worrying about doing things right. Instead, trust your instincts and create deep erotic connections with your lover.

Tantric Third-Eye Meditation Technique

Tantric practices include the use of breath, movement, sound, and meditation in order to open the energy channels in the chakra system and allow the released energy to flow from the base roots upward to reach the crown chakra. Meditation is a technique that is followed vigorously in tantric practices. The following extremely simple meditation technique can be singly or before a lovemaking session with the two partners sitting in front of each other.

The Third-Eye meditation also referred to as a Spinal Meditation, helps in opening the Crown and the Third Eye Chakras to receive divine powers from the Universe. It also facilitates the energy flow up and down the spinal cord which helps in enhancing the awareness of the Universe and its limitless powers. Moreover, this meditation also helps you remain grounded as well.

Sit comfortably either cross-legged on the floor or in a chair. If you are sitting cross-legged on the floor, feel the pressure of your bones at the base of the pelvis as it meets the cushion or floor. If you are sitting in a chair, let your feet feel the coldness of the ground.

Now, breathe in and lengthen your spinal cord in such a way like as if someone has tied a string to your spine and is pulling it in the upward direction. Then, breathe out in such a way that your tailbone is appearing to reach the floor with the length of the spine being maintained same as before. Imagine your tailbone to work like a tap root that is affixed to the earth holding a tree or plant up erect. Keep your breathing in and out at a natural pace.

Now, put the tip of your tongue on the roof of your mouth and imagine a round golden ball at the third eye chakra location (between your brows on your forehead). While inhaling through your nose, roll the golden ball to touch the Crown chakra and then let it slide down the spine right up to the tailbone. During this time, you must chant the mantra, 'hung.'

When you exhale, toss the ball upward from your tailbone and let it travel through the spine until it reaches the third eye location after touching the Crown chakra. During the upward movement of the golden ball, you must chant the mantra, 'sau' (rhyming with 'saw').

This chant translates to 'I am' or 'I am that' which means this body, mind, and spirit are part of the universal consciousness. Therefore, chanting of this mantra reaffirms your true self as being one with the Earth (rooted through the tailbone) and the Divine (which is connected via the imaginary string attached to the top of the spine). Begin this practice by doing for 5 minutes daily. Slowly, increase your duration at regular intervals until you build it up to 20 minutes every day.

Any activity that activates the energy flow in your body must necessarily be balanced by a grounding activity that keeps you rooted and stabilized. While activated chakras are great to experience higher levels of consciousness, an ever-activated energy system can be very difficult to handle at the earthly plane and to counter this, balancing and rooting activities will help you keep energy activation in check and facilitate grounding.

So, in effect, by practicing this tantric meditation, you will have access to the higher powers of this world while remaining grounded so as to leverage those powers to lead a happier and more fulfilled life than before. Practice the third-eye meditation alone first. When you are sufficiently comfortable with it, you can do this meditation technique with your partner sitting opposite each other to get into the zone of lovemaking.

Chapter Four: Yantras and Mantras

In addition to breathing and other techniques used in tantra practices, yantras and mantras are also commonly included. This chapter deals with Yantras and some of the mantras used in Tantra.

What are Yantras?

Yantra, in its literal translation from Sanskrit, means 'instrument' or a 'support.' In tantra practice, a Yantra is usually a geometrical design that is employed as a very effective tool to support the practitioner in meditative, contemplative, and concentration activities. Yantras represent the macrocosm in a microcosmic frame and acts like a gateway to and from the higher planes of consciousness. Yantras are all spiritually significant designs and every aspect has specific meanings pertaining to the higher planes of consciousness.

The Yantra in tantric practices behaves like a window to the universal divine being or the absolute one, as this power is many times referred to. When you compel your mind to focus on a single design or object (the yantra in this case), the overwhelming mental chatter that clutters your mind is reduced. With practice, it is possible to completely eliminate mindless chatter in your mind. When the mind has achieved calmness and complete stillness, the yantra is dropped by the practitioners. A seasoned tantric practitioner only needs to visualize the yantra in his mind to reach the calm state of mind.

Yantras are usually designed symmetrically in such a way that the practitioner's eyes can be focused on the center. Yantras can be drawn on paper, on wood, on metal, or directly on the earth. They can also be three-dimensional objects. In India, the most famous one is the Sri Vidya yantra that represents the deity Tripura Sundari. This symbol is a microcosm of the entire universe and is used to remind the practitioners that there is no difference between the object and the subject.

Operation of Yantras

'Form energy' of 'shape energy' or the concept that every form or shape emits a particular energy pattern and frequency, is the basis of the operation of any yantra. Examples of such yantras that are seen even in Judaism and Christianity include the 5-pointed star or the Pentagon, the Star of David, the pyramids, the Cross, etc. These shapes are given different degrees of negative and positive power (or evil and/or good power). In Tantra practices, only those shapes that have positive attributes and those with harmonious and beneficial energies are used.

When a practitioner focuses on the particular yantra, his or her mind automatically tunes in to the 'resonating' frequency or energy pattern of that yantra. Continued focus helps in maintaining and amplifying this resonating effect. It is important to remember at this point that the energy itself as a result of the focusing exercise comes from the macrocosm and not from the yantra.

Therefore, yantras are instruments or tools that help us achieve resonance with a particular frequency from the macrocosm. The yantra facilitates the practitioner to 'tune in' to the desired frequency from the macrocosm. It is possible to effectively use yantras to put the practitioner into elevated energy levels in the universe.

Types of Yantras Used in Tantric Practices

Unfortunately, the Western world is yet to understand the true meaning and the resonating power of a yantra. Many dubious tantric schools claim that they can draw Yantras by drawing on their imagination. This is not true. Every mood and every emotion has a specific yantra associated with it through the energy that its form and shape represents.

The traditional Yantras were not drawn from imagination but revealed through divine design and through clairvoyance. Revealing a new yantra to the world requires the limitless tantric powers of a true guru and taking all and sundry 'designs' available on the internet as a yantra will only reduce the power and influence of your tantric practice.

Yantras and mantras are connected in the sense that a particular yantra needs to be focused on by chanting a corresponding mantra. Here are a few yantras along with a basic understanding of each of their resonance.

The Dot or the Bindu – The Bindu represented focalized energy brought on by intense concentration. It can be seen as a deposit or reservoir of concentrated energy. In Tantric practice, the dot is considered to represent Siva Himself, the masculine source of all creation.

The Triangle or the Trikona – This is a symbol of Shakti, the feminine source of all creation. A downward pointing triangle represents the female sexual organ, the yoni, the Universe's supreme source. An upward pointing triangle represents the supreme spiritual aspiration of being one with the absolute. Also, the downward triangle represents water which tends to flow down while the upward triangle represents fire which goes UP always.

The 6-Pointed Star of the Shatkona – Two triangles, one upward-facing, and the other downward facing, superimposed over each other combine to form the shatkona, referred to as David's star in Judaism. This symbol represents the union of Siva and Shakti, without which there can be NO creation.

The Circle or the Chakra – Representing rotation, the circle is another commonly used symbol either by itself or as part of a more complex yantra in tantric practices. Rotation is also a movement that is very closely connected with spiraling movement, the basis of the evolution in the macrocosm. Moreover, the chakra or the circle is also a represented of the creative void and perfection. It symbolizes the wind element of nature.

The Lotus Symbol – This is a symbol of variety (each petal representing something different) and purity owing to the flower's ability to rise above a dirty pond to remain beautiful and pure.

The Square or the Bhupura – Representing the element earth, the square symbol is normally the external contour of a yantra. Usually, a yantra uses the square as the contour and the dot as the center. The reason for this is the concept in tantra that the universe starts from the subtle (the dot – concentrated energy) and moves toward the gross (or the earth and life systems).

Many of the complex yantras also include other symbols such as arrows, swords, tridents, etc. representing the direction and purpose of action of the form energy the yantra signifies.

How to Use Yantras in Tantric Practices

As already explained, resonance is the critical aspect of any yantra. The resonating effect of the yantra can be initiated and maintained by focusing on its image. The mind should be tuned to the resonating energy of the particular yantra for activation and sustenance of energy flow. Here are some instructions on the correct use of yantras:

Hang the Yantra on any wall facing East or North ensuring the center of the image is in line with your eyes.

When meditating, sit in a comfortable position that you are accustomed to.

Inhale through the nose and exhale through your mouth in your natural breathing rhythm without trying to control your breath.

Focus on the center of the yantra with as little blinking as possible. Keep the focus of your eyes on the center and watch the entire yantra as one.

You can start with 5 minutes each day of this meditating exercise and then, slowly increase the duration until you can do about half an hour a day.

It is recommended that you aspire to achieve the levels of resonating energy that the yantra is capable of delivering and your aspiration is bound to be fulfilled sooner than later.

Seasoned tantric practitioners can reach such amazing depths in their focus that it is difficult for them to tell whether the yantra is within them or whether they are inside the yantra.

Importance of Mantra in Tantric Practices

Chanting and practicing mantras in tantra is designed to help you achieve the dhyana state which translates to contemplate or to imagine. Meditation through mantra is not being 'lost' in thought. Instead, it an active state of mind where deep awareness can be experienced is a seamless flow of thoughts. When you achieve this meditative state, your consciousness is expanded such that space represented by Shakti unites with time represented by Siva resulting in a cosmic union, the microcosm of which is believed in tantra to be the sexual union between man and woman on earth.

Mantras are connected with the human aspect through the deity they represent or signify. Deities, in tantra practice, are also functional manifestations of the universal absolute of which we are all apart. Deities are manifested internally and externally through the human body and can be accessed by experience and/or cognition. Mantras connect the human to the particular deity. In short, mantras are a sacred formula in the form of vibrations and sounds that represent the associated deity which is a function of the entire universe.

Here are a few mantras associated with the respective deity along with the results of chanting them consistently:

Deity – Mantra – Results

Ganesha – Gam – success and protection
Kali – Krim – victory, protection, and liberation
Lakshmi – Shrim – beauty, prosperity, and wealth
Saraswati – Aim – Knowledge, arts, music, and sensibility
Shiva – Om Namah Shivaya or Hum – awareness, protection, and liberation
Shakti – Hrim – family, energy, and good moral qualities

How to Practice Mantra

When you practice mantra persistently, your mind is getting closer and closer to the vibration and sound of the mantra thereby creating a link between you and the particular deity. You should sit comfortably and recite the mantra at the same speed as your natural speech. Do not try to hurry the repetition of the mantra. Even as thoughts come and go in your mind, you must persist in pronouncing or mouthing the mantra with as little distractions as possible. You can also combine this with meditating with your yantra and focus on it while you recite your mantra.

Depending on your desired results, you can choose to change the mantra. For the desires of knowledge, use the Saraswati mantra, if you desire wealth, use the Lakshmi mantra, etc. Using mantras are a great way of bringing in your meditative powers while helping you connect with a more powerful function of the universal energy than your own.

Chapter Five: Asanas in Tantra

T he final chapter will talk about the most intimate thing of Tantric practices and that is a sexual union in order to achieve divine revelation while enhancing the love and passion in any relationship. This chapter talks about the various asanas used in tantric practice.

Whether we know it or not, love is the ultimate law of nature and everything revolves around this amazing element. Tantra yoga has been passed down by the wise sages to help couples transmit this love between themselves so that there is harmony, joy, and passion in their relationship. The asanas mentioned here can be performed anytime, but if done before lovemaking session can empower the sexual union to help achieve supreme bliss for both partners.

Navasana or the Ship's Pose

This asana is designed to specifically enhance trust between partners and let the love between the two of you become a dependable element in both your lives. Sit in front of each other and keeping your knees bent, let your soles touch those of your partner's. Hold hands. If you cannot reach each other's hands, then take the help of a scarf to hold each end.

Now, keep your spine as straight as possible and lift both your feet with your soles still in contact with each other. Start with one set of foot and then move on to the next.

Once, you have both your soul-touching feet (like palms joined together) straight above, try and keep your chest and spine as erect as you possibly can. Hold the ship pose as long as both of you can without overly straining any part of your body.

Virabhadrasana or the Hero's Pose

This asana is meant to increase the feeling of spiritual love in both of you. When you practice this pose with persistence, you will notice that as a couple you are able to overcome obstacles in a smoother and easier way than before. You will find enhanced energy levels in your body and mind helping you achieve your combined goals.

This asana has to be performed both in the right and the left sides. For the left side, here is what you do.

Face your partner and put your right foot forward. Both of you must do this resulting in your right feet touching each other along the shank on the inner side. Now, lift your arms and bring the palms forward facing each other so that your right palm is in full contact with the right palm of your lover and the left palms are also touching the same way. Press the palms tightly together.

Now, put your left foot back as if you are taking a huge step with the ankle making a 45-degree angle with the ground. Keep the soles of both your feet firmly on the ground. The right knee should be bent so as to form a right angle. Breathe calmly and look with passion into your partner's eyes. Come out of this asana slowly and deliberately pulling back each part of your hands and legs to their normal positions. Now, do the same on the right side which will entail you to put your left foot forward and your right foot back.

The V Letter

This asana is meant to take your trust and intimacy to even further levels. Holding on to each other's wrists, bend as much backward as you can with the trust that your partner will not let go of your wrists and that you will not let go of your partner's wrists. This pose will ideally result in the letter V being formed by your two bodies.

Focus on the flow of energy between yourselves through the connected arms. The more you resonate with each other's energy, the more you will find it easy to balance the other in the pose. Continued practice will help in improving the ability of both partners to resonate with the energy of the other partner and this will build enhanced trust and intimacy between the two of you.

Vrikshasana or the Tree Pose

The pose is designed to help couples increase their capability to view and achieve higher goals and ideals in their combined lives. The two partners will be able to achieve higher planes of consciousness by acceding to each other's high ideals.

Stand next to each other with a little bit of gap between the two of you. Place the arm that is closest to your partner around his or her waist. So, here, one partner will have the left arm around the other partner's waist and the latter will have the right arm around the former's waist.

Now, lift the leg that is farther away from your partner and bend the knee and bring the foot forward to touch the inner respective thigh. Next, bring the arm that is away from the partner over your respective head and touch your partner's palm so as to fully be in contact. Come out of the asana slowly and deliberately. Repeat on the other side so that the left and right sides of both partners are equally used.

The Bicycle Pose

Lie on your backs with the knees bent and facing each other. Now, bend your knees and take it up to your chest and let your partner do the same ensuring that the soles of your feet are in contact fully. Place the weight of your body on your lower backs. Keep your hands away as they are not needed for this asana. Intertwining the fingers and placing them under your neck would be a comfortable position for your hands. So, now both of you are on your backs with the knees close to or touching your chest and the soles of your feet in full contact.

Breathe for a while and once you get your rhythm with your partner, start the pedaling action with the soles still in touch. As you change the leg which is pedaling, you can shift your torso appropriately keeping your abdominal muscles as stiff as possible. Breathe in through your nose and breathe out through your mouth, each time the torso needs to be shifted during the pedaling action. You will feel a wonderful sense of dynamism and joy pervading both of you and the effervescence will be unmistakable. Come out of the asana slowly.

Ustrasana or the Camel Pose

This asana facilitates the couple to achieve a sense of euphoria combined with empathy as both of your inner willpower harmonizes with each other. Kneel and face your partner as he or she does the same thing facing toward you. Now, holding each other's elbow, bend backward without putting stress on your neck muscles. Ensure your knee is kept at a 90-degree angle. Feel the energies flowing between your bodies through the connecting arms.

If you notice, each of these poses can also be done alone, individually. So, do them individually until each of you has achieved perfection in the asanas. Then, as per tantric practices, combine the yoga performance and do them as a couple. Here are some amazing benefits of performing yoga together as a couple, especially before lovemaking sessions:

- It helps in creating a genuine and deep connection between the couples and these deep bonds help you go beyond customary ties and with practice can help you achieve union at a much higher consciousness than the human level.

- It can deepen and enhance your spiritual, physical, psychic, erotic, and mental connections with each other in unimaginable ways.

- Performing yoga as a couple has the power to bring in harmony, beauty, refinement, and sheer strength to the relationship.

- Your relationship will be able to reflect each other's deepest secrets and desires that were hitherto obscure to both of you. Couple yoga helps you manifest your deepest desire to your partner and vice versa and that too, without fear of embarrassment, being judged, or anything else that forms the basest aspect of humankind.

- A beautiful relationship borne out of doing couple yoga can not only help in uplifting your own souls but also help in improving the interactions and relationships of other people in and around your personal and professional life.

- In addition to yoga, if the partners indulge in sexual continence, then the ensuing release of energy will cover a wider sphere of people. Just like how a little candle can radiate light in any dark room, similarly, true love can radiate happiness unconditionally everywhere.

Chapter Six: Tantric Sexual Techniques

Now, that you understand why tantra uses the sexual union as the way to achieve divine enlightenment; let us look as at some of the sexual techniques proposed by tantric sex positions that will help you achieve happiness along with supreme sexual pleasure, many times with continence too. So, here goes.

Before you get into the actual act, the following tips will ensure your sexual encounters are fulfilling and deeply satisfying for both of you:

Choose a convenient day – Tantric sex does not involve a 10-12 minute thrust in-thrust out technique. It is slow and sensual and takes time. Choose a day that is convenient to both partners and ensures that there is a commitment of 2 hours to the entire exercise. Once, the time is fixed and committed by both partners; it is important to feel disciplined and not put off the scheduled event. Even if you are tired, get started, and watch your fatigue melt into nothingness as you experience rejuvenating love.

Be open to try new and novel techniques – For successful tantric sex practices, it is very important to keep an open heart and open mind. The act is not relegated to some form of cheap sex. It is divine and an act that has the power to energize and change the perspective of the partners towards who they are and what the world is. For this, you must be ready and open to trying new and novel things that you have not tried before. Free yourself from conditioned shackles.

Set the right mood – Light scented candles or incense and make the room sensual and nice. It would help if you can have a refreshing, scented bath as well. Give each other compliments by telling what you like in the other. Do not hesitate to look deeply into each other's eyes and try to see beyond what the eyes seem to show you. Delve deep and find that connection between the two of you.

Meditate together – Using some of the techniques listed in this book, meditate together by sitting in front of each other. Looking at each other's bodies without actually touching can be a highly pleasurable experience and also will help you understand each other's strengths and weaknesses.

You could simply sit and breathe deeply and attempt to synchronize your breaths. With practice, you can include yantras and mantras to enhance the feeling of togetherness as you meditate and feel each other's spiritual, emotional, and physical presence more acutely than before.

Perform a few couple yoga asanas – Considering the immense benefits of performing yoga together; it makes a lot of sense to do a couple of asanas together and get even closer to each other physically and spiritually than before.

Get intimate with each other by sitting in the Yab-Yum pose – The Yab-Yum pose has been designed to enhance intimacy between the partners in some amazingly unimaginable ways. Sitting in this position, your souls and hearts can merge together to achieve supreme bliss. The man has to sit cross-legged on the floor or on the bed. The woman has to sit on her man's lap. Let her wrap her legs around his waist and her arms around his neck. The pose can be performed either with clothes on or in the naked form. The choice is entirely both of yours make.

In this position, embrace each other deeply and try and synchronize your breathing again. Allow your bodies to feel and tune in to each other and feel your heart and soul merging in this beautiful and loving embrace that can be devoid of all sexual feeling but totally filled with feelings of love, joy, and togetherness.

Hold on for as long as you want to feel each other's love, breath, and happiness. It can be a very special moment for both partners. This pose is excellent to celebrate your unique and beautiful relationship. You can kiss in this position to feel the love even deeper.

Give each other a good massage – Again, taking the tips and ideas given in this book, take turns to be the giver and receiver of the massage and enjoy each other's touch. You can start from non-erotic positions like the neck, back, arms, etc., and slowly and gradually, move your fingers and hands to do their magic right through all parts of receiver's body. Do not forget to take and receive feedback so that the receiver remains in the joy of the massage instead of letting his or her thoughts fly somewhere else.

Now, let us look at some basic tantric sex positions for you to try tonight itself:

Position 1

The male partner should kneel behind the female while tilting slightly backward. The female should have her back to the male and should also kneel down with legs tucked between his legs. Now, both of your sit down on your calves and thighs ensuring your bodies are tightly squeezed together.

Let the male partner wrap his arms around the female partner's waist holding her tightly to his body. Now, let his penis get inside you and once he is inside, do the tilt and tuck movement together. You can also do circular movements together. When you are tired, take breaks by simply sitting in the same position holding your bodies tightly squeezed together.

As the male partner is tilting slightly backward, he will be able to reach the female's G-spot which is, perhaps, one of the most pleasurable spots for a woman. Moreover, as the female's butt is tightly squeezed to his thighs, his groin will fit snugly inside you enhancing the pleasure for both of you.

Position 2

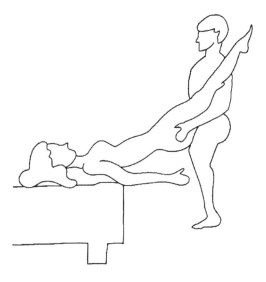

Let the female partner lie on her back at the edge of the bed, tabletop, or any other countertop with a pillow under her back for a bit of elevation. She must extend her legs in the upward direction so that her opening is right at the edge of the bed or table. Keeping the legs straight up will be very beneficial for the entire act. She can use her hands to keep her legs raised higher so that her pelvis is also raised.

Now, the male partner can enter the female while standing or kneeling down if the table is very low. Holding the female straightened legs will give him leverage while helping the female get balance too. He can now thrust inside with added stability for both the partners. It is important to keep the female legs as much as possible together.

Keeping the legs close together gives you a very tight fit ensuring there is sufficient and blissful friction during the tilt and tuck motion of the lovemaking session. Loosening the female legs and getting them back tightly together will give added pleasure to both of the partners.

Position 3

Let the woman stand at the edge of the bed or couch with feet and legs wide apart. The man will stand on the floor with the feet firmly on the ground very close to his woman, facing her. Adjusting the width of the woman's stance, the man can find the right position to get inside her so that both their pelvises touch each other. Now, do the tilt and tuck motion together to feel the supreme bliss of being inside each other.

The stability of this pose enhances pleasure for both of you without worrying about the stress on any body part. Moreover, legs wide apart make the woman feel vulnerable which only enhances the love of the man for his woman. The continuous friction on the front side is sure to hit the g-spot of the woman which, enhances her pleasure to great heights.

As both the partners are standing, there is very little to hold back. The hands will be free to do other erotic activities on each other's bodies resulting in added pleasure during the entire process.

When both are satiated and happy with the entire ritual, you can indulge in the yab-yum pose again before giving up these wonderful moments of togetherness. The energy release during a tantric sex ritual does not enervate. It invigorates you and your partner to take and receive more from each other and the universe, at large. Remember to give 100% of yourselves to the other partner.

Conclusion

One of the primary principles of Tantra is there is no form of energy in the Universe that does not exist in our body. Tantra also means technique and it is that which helps us leverage the different forms of energy available in our body in a conscious way so that there is increased productivity in your life.

Although the secrets of the Tantra tradition was kept a secret for hundreds of years for multiple reasons including the chances of them being misunderstood and misinterpreted, today, thanks to the internet and the world becoming a global village, more and more people are clearing their heads of misunderstandings and are given themselves to the magic of this system to lead a more fulfilled, happy, and healthy lifestyle than before.

Tantric traditions and their rituals are designed to draw out the subtle energies in our body and work with them to alleviate the practitioner both physically and spiritually. Tantric practices empower you to explore and leverage the power within you while eliminating physical and mental blocks that prevent you from achieving your best.

Remember that we are all born as Tantric lovers because we are all part of the ultimate divine. We are the pure presence if only we could find the power and wherewithal to tear away the layers that have been laid on this pure essence through years of mistaken conditioning. Again, sex is definitely a part of tantric practices; but tantra sex is founded on pure love that is the basis of the pure essence drawn from the omnipresent divine.

Tantra practices are designed to help you connect with yourself, with your partner, and with the divine. Tantra is a potent combination of spirituality and sexuality to help us understand ourselves better thereby empowering us to lead more fulfilling, contented, and lives, irrespective of our social standing, our gender, our caste, our race, our nationality, or anything else.

Living a life based on Tantric practices helps us achieve balance through the integration of feminine and masculine aspects of ourselves so that we feel a sense of wholesome that is presently lacking in our lives. Tantric practices help us see the divine in everything around us. These practices (if done patiently and diligently) infuse our senses and bodies with copious amounts of unbridled and unconditional love and compassion for one and all.

Additionally, when we practice Tantra, we are rid of baseless shame, guilt, and embarrassment associated with our sexuality that are again built around insensitive conditioning of our society. So, bringing in Tantra into your life translates to more love, compassion, and an increased sense or perception of the divine.

Tantric practices also help you use the preserved energy to find your true purpose. Of course, it is important to start small, begin with the simple individual and couple techniques mentioned in this book (which can be started immediately) and once you have mastered the simple ones and drawn the amazing benefits of even these simple tantric practices, you can move on and learn more advanced techniques from reputable teachers and take your life to an entirely new level of consciousness.

One last thing. We would be super happy if you took the time to give us some feedback so we can improve the book. You can do that by posting a review on the Amazon product page. Thank you very much in advance!

Resources

https://medium.com/@matthiasrose/the-origins-of-tantra-acc4334638e9
https://psiloveyou.xyz/tantra-shmantra-d52c6a35923d
http://www.oztantra.com/tantric-history-2/
http://www.yogamag.net/archives/1981/joct81/womrole.shtml
https://www.healthcentral.com/article/the-spiritual-and-health-benefits-of-tantra-yoga
http://www.stylecraze.com/articles/tantric-yoga-benefits/#gref   http://www.anamayaresort.com/tantra-yoga-benefits/
https://www.mindbodygreen.com/0-17370/a-tantra-meditation-to-enhance-your-love-life.html
https://www.mindbodygreen.com/0-17733/6-practices-to-awaken-the-tantric-lover-within.html
https://www.elephantjournal.com/2017/08/5-ways-to-begin-practicing-tantra/
http://www.sivasakti.com/tantra/introduction-to-yantra/
http://www.spirit-web.org/yoga/tantra-yoga/the-practice-of-tantric-mantras
http://www.allabouttantra.info/en/english/52-couple-asanas
http://www.cosmopolitan.com/tantric-sex-positions/
https://mytinysecrets.com/tantra-101-a-super-simple-guide-for-tantric-sex-beginners/

CPSIA information can be obtained
at www.ICGtesting.com
Printed in the USA
BVHW070836130223
658300BV00014B/441